TITLE II-A

Other Books by Maia Wojciechowska

Shadow of a Bull
Awarded the 1965 Newbery Medal

Odyssey of Courage

A Kingdom in a Horse

The Hollywood Kid

A Single Light

Tuned Out

"Hey, What's Wrong With This One?"

"DON'T PLAY DEAD BEFORE YOU HAVE TO"

HARPER & ROW, PUBLISHERS
NEW YORK, EVANSTON, AND LONDON

"DON'T PLAY DEAD BEFORE YOU HAVE TO"

A novel

by Maia Wojciechowska

for John Tunis,
who won all the major battles,
and for Karen,
because she is learning well how to fight them

"In such a fantastic and dangerous world—we will not find answers in old dogmas, by repeating outworn slogans, or fighting on ancient battlegrounds against fading enemies long after the real struggle has moved on. We ourselves must change to master change. We must rethink all our old ideas and beliefs before they capture and destroy us. . . . America must look to its young people, the children of this time of change. And we look especially to that privileged minority of educated men who are the students of America."

—Robert F. Kennedy

"DON'T
PLAY DEAD
BEFORE
YOU HAVE TO"

Summer and Fourteen

O.K., kid, I'm here to baby-sit for you and I don't want
any trouble out of you. We're going to get along just
fine if you stay on your side of the fence. What do I
mean? Look, kid, I'm a loner. I'm not about to make
friends with you or anything like that, see? I'm getting
paid to sit for you and that's it. I don't intend to be
your pal or anything.

Hey, how old are you anyway? Five? That's all?
What's your name again? Charlie? I thought your
mother said something like . . . Charlemagne, yeah.
Well, I don't blame you for calling yourself Charlie.
Where did you get a queer name like Charlemagne
from? That's O.K., I don't want to know the history
of the western world with all the gory details. Shake.

3

My name's Byron. I don't know—Byron's not half as queer a name as Charlemagne. Yeah, come to think of it, when I was your age, kid, I hated my name too. Was I ever a dumb kid! No, that's all right, you go right ahead and change your name as often as you want. There ain't a law that says that you got to be saddled with a dumb name just because your mother gave it to you when you were too young to object. No, you can't call yourself Byron. Because that happens to be my name, for God's sake!

What're you doing having your dinner this late? God, we're through by six. Hey, what's that junk on your plate? A what? A cheese soufflé? Never heard of it. Yeah, let's have a taste. I guess I would have survived without ever tasting the stuff. How come you eat queer stuff like that? Your mother's trying French recipes on you? How much do you get for letting her practice on you? Nothing! You sure are a dumb kid. It ought to be worth at least a dime a try. After all, it's your stomach against her money.

Listen, kid, if we get along real well together I wouldn't mind sitting for you again. The thing is I need to save up for a car and I just got fired by this guy I used to mow the lawn for. He claimed I ran the mower over his wife's flower garden. He was a creep anyway—always worrying about the weeds taking over as if they were a bunch of his personal enemies or something. Anyway, I'd rather baby-sit because nobody's telling you what to do and that's one thing I can't stand—some dummy telling me what to do.

4

Oh, yeah? Your parents always play bridge on Saturday nights? Sure, I'll sit for you. Forever? Well, I don't know about that. By the time you get to be my age it would look real queer having a baby-sitter. Well, sure, I should hope so! If I weren't better than some dumb girl I wouldn't have very much going for me.

Not much. As a matter of fact I've only got thirteen-fifty saved. But I won't be getting a license for another two years, eleven months, and four days. Sure I keep score. I've got this calendar I made and every day I cross one day off. Getting a car is about the most important thing in a guy's life. The way I figure it there is nothing important that can happen in a guy's life until he gets a driver's license.

You know how to write and how to count? How come? Look, kid, you're only five, right? What the hell do you want to be so smart at your age for? When I was five I was just beginning to learn how to wave bye-bye. If you don't mind, let's not talk about school. I've just finished eight years at the lousiest Catholic school in the world. Boy, those nuns were sure a bunch of winners! No, stupid, that's not what I mean. Just the opposite.

Yeah, I'll be going to high school in September. A public school. Are you kidding? I'll hate it. Because school stinks. Don't kid yourself, kid, you won't like it. It's all a waste of time and if I were you I wouldn't even go to kindergarten. I wouldn't even bother starting school at all. I wouldn't even let on that I'm alive. See, if they don't have you filed away in some record book they wouldn't know you existed and they couldn't make you go to school. Ever. Why? I told you, kid, all they do in school is wreck your mind.

Hey, you finished yet? O.K., let's go and watch some TV. What do you mean you don't have a TV set? Everybody's got a TV. You're kidding me, right? It's in a repair shop, right? Your parents won't buy one? What are they, some kinds of nuts? How the hell do they expect anybody normal to sit for you without a TV? I'll go crazy, for God's sake!

Games! What kind of games? Grow up, kid. I'm not about to play any dumb games with you and I'll never sit for you again, and that's a promise. Hey, cut it out! What are you crying for? Wipe your nose. Not on your sleeve, stupid. Well, go to the john and get some.

That's better. O.K., kid, let's get to the bottom of this thing. The thing is we've got to con your parents into buying a set, because otherwise I'm not sitting for you and I'd like to. I'm not mad at *you*! I'm mad at them! Just tell me this, kid, what's the reason they gave you for not having a TV set? Bad for you? What the hell do you mean bad for you? You must be kidding! Look, kid, all I know I've learned from watching television. Like what? Like everything! Hey, you got a couple of toy guns around? You're kidding me again, right? You don't have to love war to have toy guns around, for God's sake! What kind of a kid are they trying to make out of you? Every kid in the world has to have toy guns; how the hell do they expect you to learn how to draw? Not pictures, stupid! A draw, a draw! Forget it!

6

You know something, kid, you ain't going to make it in life. You ain't going to grow up right, or have a friend or . . . Cut it out! The hell with Kleenex! Just get a roll of toilet paper and bring it here. You've got a lot to learn and if learning makes you bawl that's not my fault.

Oh, man, I got here just in time. Another couple of months and the little kid would be beyond help.

Hey, what are you doing? What are you washing dishes for? That's your mother's job, not yours. You're a little kid and she gets paid for things like housework. Same thing, she gets free room and board, doesn't she? Come on, let's go to the living room.

Hey, what are those things all about—the paintings? Your father does them? Is he famous? Well, that's tough. Maybe he ought to paint them so people could understand them. That's your favorite? What is it? An atomic what? Holocaust? How do you spell it? Forget it, kid. You kidding me again? You really know how to spell it? To tell you the honest truth, kid, you're beginning to depress me. Hey, you sure you're only five? The way I figure it you might be a midget or something.

Look kid, don't start crying or anything, but I've got to level with you. You're not going to make it in life if you're this smart so early. A little kid is supposed to be nice and dumb. It's like a free ride; you're entitled to it and if you miss it you'll be in trouble. Nobody wants a little kid to be smart, don't you get that? No, I wouldn't say you're smarter than me!

The thing is you're entitled to a few more things—

like having a TV and not doing dishes and ... Do me a favor, will you, don't tell me what your mother tells you. I've got one of my own and she tells me plenty I don't care to hear.

So what am I supposed to do with you, kid? Do you realize that I haven't spent one single solitary evening without a television since I was born? Hey, kid, who spoils you more, your dad or your mom? You don't know? You better figure it out or else you won't know who to con first. You've got to con your parents into things. It's the only way of getting ahead in life.

Let's take your dad first. What does he want you to be? When you grow up, stupid. Sorry. You're pretty touchy, aren't you? Of course you're not stupid! I only wish you were. Well, let me make a couple of guesses. Your father wants you to become a great ball player. Because all fathers want their sons to become great ball players, that's why. Sure, mine does too. He wants me to support him in the style he never got accustomed to. He's a bus driver. Oh, he's O.K. He boozes a lot and he's got this crazy idea that every time he opens his mouth to me he's got to say something I should remember on my deathbed or something. He calls them "words to live by," and I have an idea he steals them from *Reader's Digest*. Like what? Well, they always fit something I'm doing. Like I was washing my hands last night and he was waiting for me to clear out of the bathroom, so he says, "Always keep your hands clean and nobody will call you a thief." I don't know. He thinks it makes sense and who am I to make him unhappy? So I always say, gee, dad, that one I sure will pass on to my kids. That really makes it for him.

If you want to survive you've got to figure out how to con your parents. The best way is to do something dumb such as play Little League. Boy, do those kids always get everything they want! But to do that you've got to work like hell and be ambitious and aggressive and all that crap. Never could do it myself. But maybe you could. No, I'd rather you didn't. Kids who play Little League grow up real ugly and what's worse they bring the worst out in their parents. But I bet your dad would like that; he'd like you to play ball. Tennis! Ahh, same thing! So he wants you to be a hotshot tennis player when you grow up. So, you make a deal with him, he gives you a television set and you ask him for a tennis racket. That will get him right in the gut. Oh, come on! You already got a tennis racket?

Hey, I'm tired of thinking about conning your parents, you do that on your own time and it's O.K. with me how you do it as long as there is a TV around here by next Saturday. Say, how about getting me some potato chips and a Coke. What do you mean you ain't got no Coke? You sure you're Americans? How about potato chips? Hell! Listen, kid, by next Saturday, besides that TV set, I want a carton of Cokes and garlic-flavored potato chips around here or I ain't coming to sit for you. You got that straight?

Oh, boy, just look at me, I'm a nervous wreck. Nothing to do. Hey, hand me that phone and the phone book. Relax, I'm going to play a dumb game I haven't played in a couple of years. Shut up, it's ringing. Hallo, is this Mrs. Woods? Mrs. Woods, you are one of the select few we are calling to offer a new product. We call it "brains." Yes, ma'am, brains. Well, we at Mary Poppins Associates feel that nobody should be without our product and you have been recommended by your neighbors in our recent survey. No, ma'am, it's not some kind of a joke. You see, the way it works is this. You can use our product free and without any obligation on your part for thirty days. If you are not satisfied . . . Mrs. Woods? Oh, damn, she hung up on me!

Let's try this number . . . May I speak to your daddy? Well, how about your mommy—is she home? What are you doing home all alone? How old are you anyway? Is there anyone else there with you? A baby? Look, kid, you sure you're O.K.? They leave you alone a lot? A punishment! They're punishing you by leaving you and your sister alone? I think I'll report your parents to the police. They wouldn't dare beat you! I'd be the one calling the police. Well, look, kid, here is the number I'm calling you from . . . No, I didn't want anything. You got a pencil? O.K. My name's Byron. Doesn't matter how you spell it. The number here is 337-7049. Yeah, I'll be here until late. And look, kid, if you ever need someone to talk to or something you better write down my number at home. 337-7331. But you sure you're all right? How long have they been leaving you alone like that? Hey, if you ever feel like running away from home you just call me. And kid, don't be scared of them. They can't do nothing to you. There must be some laws and they'd be in trouble. And don't let them beat you up. Promise? O.K., kid, so call me. Anytime.

Boy, how do you like that! That kid was only seven and he's minding his baby sister and they're all alone, for God's sake! That really depressed the hell out of me. I can just see them. I bet they're poor and everything and I bet those lousy parents are boozing somewhere and are going to come home and I bet they'll beat those kids up. Just the other night my old man was reading in the paper that there are thousands of little kids being killed by insane parents, and thousands who are beat up and burned and stuff. God, that makes me madder than anything! I mean, what the hell can a little kid do for himself? A little kid doesn't know about laws and stuff. What the hell was that kid's number? Oh, shit, I closed the phone book and now I don't know how to reach him. What would I do? I'd go out to his house and case his parents. I mean, he might be one of those little kids whose parents are sadists.

Hey, kid, what time are you supposed to go to sleep anyway? What do you mean not until you feel like it? They've got a hell of a lot of things mixed up. Sure they're supposed to tell you what time you've got to go to bed. It's what keeps them busy, making up rules like that. But your mother shouldn't make you do dishes because that'd be taking your valuable time away from the TV.

You just moved in, right? Where did you come from?

You lived in Europe—for a whole year! Boy, are you ever lucky. Your father was . . . Teaching painting? Some teacher he must've been! Oh, yeah? I knew there was bound to be something strange about your mother. Mothers aren't supposed to be writing novels. How are you going to grow up into a normal kid with parents like that? Don't start crying again, for God's sake! I'll stick around and help you. O.K., don't get slobbery. What do you mean you'd like to grow up to be like me? Don't kid yourself, kid, you can do much better than that.

You think you've got problems! Just look at me! I can't even get along with anybody and that's because everybody I meet seems like a creep to me. I used to have one friend and he moved away. And you know what, he had this kid sister your age, and I liked her better than him. How do you like that? Do you realize I practically didn't graduate from the dumb grammar school? Twice a month, like clockwork, I had to carry this note to my parents and they had to sign it. It said: "Byron is a disruptive influence on the class." It means that I knew more than my teachers and they knew it. And girls! Me and girls! Forget it! So what do you want to be like me for?

Hey, what the hell are you doing? Quit hanging on me! What do you mean you love me? Don't slobber all over me, for Christ sake! Boys don't kiss boys. Sure I like you. You're a cute kid, and don't worry about a thing. I will see to it that you make it.

What do you want to know things about me for?

No, I've never been any place except for New York City a couple of times and once to the Catskills, but that was a stupid mistake because I almost drowned in some lousy lake. I was about your age and I wasn't too bright. I didn't figure you had to learn how to swim. Hey, you swim? No? I'll teach you. You might be building a swimming pool! No kidding!

A best seller? What is it, some dirty book or something? What's the title? Nope, never heard of it but I'll ask my aunt Jean. She reads all kinds of stuff. They're going to make a movie out of it! No kidding! Well, maybe your mother isn't as dumb as I thought. Who's going to be in it, do you know? Let me know if you hear. Sure I want to see where your mother works. You might as well give me the tour of the house.

You know, this room I really dig. I sure wish we had a fireplace at our house. One day I'm going to start reading books like these. I always mean to but never get around to it. If I had a room like that I'd just stay in it and read and look into the fire. Yeah, one day you can come over and see my house. It will take you about thirty seconds to go through it at a slow pace. Boy, you must be loaded! How come you don't have no servants to baby-sit for you? Well, I'm happy you don't have them either.

Yeah, that's some studio your dad's got! Does he sell any of this stuff? Look, I'm only fourteen but if your mother is a success and your father is not, I smell trouble. Then why doesn't he paint so people could under-

13

stand what he's painting? What? You're kidding! You mean that he thinks it's too realistic? For who? Oh, boy! One day I got to talk to your dad.

Hey, that's real neat! Regulation size and everything. You? Yeah, let's see you beat me. How you going to get your nose over the edge of the table? Oh, a little stool! Well, kid, you sure you want to play me? Me break? No, you go right ahead. Hey, that's nice. You sure were lucky—two balls in, eh? What are you trying to do, kid, impress me? Do you mind getting your little stool off my big foot? Thanks. Say, do I ever get a chance to play? Oh, forget it! I don't feel like playing anyway. I hate to see a little kid like you hustling pool. Let's get out of here. It depresses me. Sure, I'll play you one day —when you don't feel like showing off.

Why don't we skip the upstairs. I really don't feel up to seeing the rest of the house. Next time, maybe. Hey, you sure you weren't putting me on about the Cokes? O.K., but don't forget to tell her.

What do you want to know about my mother for? Mom just keeps the house for us. Yeah, I'm an only kid, like you. And she bugs me, but she's no worse than most mothers. Last year I laid down the law to her and we've been getting along much better. Well, for one thing I don't let her go into my room, except once a week to clean up. I keep it locked because I don't want her snooping around. Well, some magazines and some stuff I wrote down that I don't want her to see. It's just a whole bunch of things I wrote down once when I tried to figure out what the whole big deal is all

14

about. What deal? I don't know—being alive and stuff like dying.

Why the hell should I know what I want to be? I'm only fourteen. You do? An astronaut. Forget it, kid. Because it's stupid to want to be an astronaut. They're just polluting things up there. It ought to be left alone. And besides, all those astronauts are just a bunch of boring morons. I don't mean that. Don't you get it, kid, when I call somebody stupid or a moron it doesn't have anything to do with what they know. It's what they are.

Hey, what time is it anyway? Let's go to the kitchen and see if you've got anything in the icebox I can eat without puking. That sure is a swell kitchen you've got; you ought to see mine. But mom sure is a great cook. She gives us hot dogs and hamburgers all the time. My old man and I, we both like them. And on Sunday, we have chicken or ham or something fancy like that. Hey, what's that stuff? Caviar? Ugh! I don't care if it's expensive, it stinks. Do I want some of what? Anchovies? Look, kid, don't you have anything normal around like a hot dog? How about making me a bacon and tomato on toast? You don't know how? Well, watch me. Where's the bread? What! You haven't got any normal white bread? What's that stuff shaking all over. She makes Jell-O with chicken inside? Oh, boy! What's that? A mango? I thought that was some kind of an old-fashioned dance they used to do. Where's the milk? You have no Coke and you hate milk. So what do you drink, champagne? Tea! Ugh!

Sure, I told you I'll sit for you on Saturdays. No, I couldn't sit for you every night! When I start school in September I'm going to get me a job at the supermarket after school. Sure I shave. Twice a week. Those things? Are they that bad? They're zits. You ought to see some of the guys who really have them. Mine aren't so bad.

You've got what? A girl friend! Don't you know they're stupid? All girls. What do you want to do, grow up queer? Play with guys; don't pal around with girls. Hey, what are you doing? Leave those dishes alone. I told you already. It's her job. Besides, it's time you hit the hay.

Say, that's a pretty neat room you've got. I don't mean great; I mean neat. What do you want to be so neat for? Let's throw some things around so we know somebody lives in this joint. Well, don't go too wild, kid. That's enough out of your closet. Let's get some of those toys off the shelves. Now, that looks much better. What's that? Yeah, let's see your microscope. That's beautiful! What is it? Your blood! No kidding. No, I don't care to prick my finger. My blood's probably the same as your blood. No, I don't want to see fresh blood —no thanks. Hey, don't do that! Didn't that hurt? What did you do that for? You don't have to do things like that for me, kid. Sure it looks swell but how about putting a Band-Aid or something on that finger?

O.K., wash up. You take a bath every night? What the hell for? Look, kid, in the thirteenth century people took a bath only three times in their lives—when they were born, when they got married, and when they died. So, if you take a bath once a week you'd be way ahead of them, right? Boy, that's a nice bathroom you've got. You should see ours. That's enough behind the ears, you'll rub your brain out if you wash too much. Who taught you how to brush your teeth like that? A dentist friend? You must be kidding; nobody's got a dentist for a friend. You know what? I haven't been to a dentist for four years and as far as I'm concerned they can all go to hell.

You want me to read you a story? All those books really yours? I've never seen so many books outside of a library. Let's see. You got any favorites? I don't really go for animal stories that much. You got any about little kids? I know! I'll make one up for you, O.K.? Don't rush me. I've never told a story before. What do you want it to be about? Sure, kids—but what about them? You're no help.

O.K., kid, here it goes.

Once upon a time there was this kingdom and it was all made up of little kids. There were no adults—just little kids, and they all had a real great time, all the time. They never grew to be older than seven, and they were never any younger than three. Don't ask dumb questions. It's a story; it doesn't have to be all explained or anything. Just shut up and listen.

So, anyway, there was this kingdom of kids. And they took turns at being the king. And the king could do any weird thing he wanted to. Like, once, this kid who wore glasses, he made it a law for everybody to wear glasses—even trees and animals and things. Like

17

a table would have to wear glasses and a cow had to wear glasses and just about everything had to wear glasses. And nobody liked that much. As a matter of fact they didn't like that kid at all and they just waited for him to stop being their king. The next kid who got to be king—he liked the color red—so everything and everybody had to be red. And that wasn't fun either.

But there was this kid and his name was Charlemagne. Yeah, just like your name. And when Charlemagne got his turn at being king he said, "Let's have some adults around here." But nobody knew what those were. So when they came—first a whole bunch of parents, then a whole bunch of teachers—the kids looked them over and decided they looked real weird. What are they so tall for? Why are their clothes so funny looking? they wanted to know. And when the adults began to talk, the kids couldn't make out what they were saying. Mostly they yelled at the kids. The kids were never yelled at before so at first they laughed, thinking it was pretty funny. But as time went by they got used to being yelled at, and pushed around, and even hit by the adults. Pretty soon the adults were running the whole show. And they began to have wars and they began to care for money and things—and nobody was playing games and having much fun anymore. The kids all had to study and they forgot what it used to be like before the adults came over.

And now the kids couldn't even be kings anymore. "A king's got to be someone old and wise," the adults told them. "A king's got a serious job to do." So they elected an adult king. And because he thought the kingdom was too small, he got himself a whole army and took over the kingdom next door.

The kids had to do the dishes and make beds and go to school and mow lawns and they didn't have time to do anything like play games. And pretty soon they noticed something strange. They were all growing old and there were no more kids left. They were all adults in this kingdom now.

So, the moral of the story is, kid, don't grow up too fast because you're going to get to be an adult soon enough and if it's the lousiest story you ever heard don't complain to me about it. What do you mean that was the best story you ever heard?

A secret? What kind of a secret? O.K., whisper it in my ear; but what do you want to do that for? There's nobody around. Sure I will. I'll leave it wide open. I used to be like that too, kid. I could never get to sleep unless there was some light around. As a matter of fact, I think I'll lay down right here on the other bed and go to sleep myself. What the hell else is there to do without television?

Yeah, yeah, yeah. I'll sit for you. Next Saturday for sure.

No! I told you already—not forever! Because we don't! We don't live in no lousy kingdom where nobody grows up.

I love you too, for Christ sake! Now go to sleep, will ya?

Fall and Fifteen

Look, Charlie, if you don't cut that out I won't be coming around anymore to sit for you. Well, how would you like it if you were fifteen and each and every Saturday night instead of having a ball, you had to baby-sit for a dumb little kid who jumps you the second you come into his house? No, you can't hug me either! And don't even show me you like me, for God's sake. You've got to start playing it cool, man. Why? Because guys aren't suppose to get all emotional and stuff. Stop asking me why; just take my word for it. You know what, kid? Last year you were a lot smarter than this year. Last year you did what I told you and didn't bug me with so many questions. You can learn from just listening to me; that's how you can learn. And I am telling you to play it cool.

What did you do it for? Don't you know it embarrassed the hell out of me when you snuck up on me at the drug store and started hugging me? This stupid girl from my school was there and about half of the lousy town. Sure, we're friends. But I don't want the whole rotten world to know about it. No, I'm not ashamed of you. It's part of playing it cool, for God's sake. You don't let anyone in on things like who your friends are or anything.

Sure, I play it cool all the time now. I mean, you're not going to ever see me get all excited about anything. What do you mean I do? Well you make me mad!

What the hell are you watching Channel Two for? Don't just stand there like a dummy. There is a Western on Channel Nine. Boy, don't you ever look up anything in *TV Guide*? If there is a Western with the Duke you don't turn some lousy show on, you watch the Duke. You don't like him? You ain't got a choice there, kid. You like Westerns, you've got to like the Duke. It's like a law.

Hey, just watch it. Watch the way he moves. See? It's all in the hips. I've got it pat, right? What do you mean I waddle? Ducks waddle; the Duke walks! Oh, shut up, will ya?

You know what? I've got a real good chance of making varsity. This guy, playing defensive tackle, he's moving away next month and they've got to replace him. And who's up for it? Yeah, no kidding. Sure, you can come to all our games. But I don't want you to make a fool of yourself and come up and kiss me while I'm intercepting a pass. And I don't want you to be

21

hanging around during practice or anything like that.

Oh, hell, I probably won't make varsity anyway. Yesterday I told the coach I thought he stunk. It's not funny. He doesn't stink the way you think he does. He's a sort of a rotten human being. Because he was making fun of this big dumb kid.

Hey, look, kid. Just watch this part. Now, this guy, he's the Duke's friend, see? He really digs him, but look how they talk to each other. Watch it, stupid. So, how do they act? Like they barely know each other, right? Now, that's what I was talking about—how to play it cool.

What's that you got behind your back? Hey, they look great! They look like real six-shooters. How come you got them? For us to have around all the time? Sure, I'll draw against you. Let's see you, first. Pretty good. But you ain't seen nothing. Give it here. Now, look, kid. There's different ways you can wear your guns. But the best way—the way the Duke wears them—is low, so that you only barely have to bend your elbows to reach. The thing is speed, right? O.K., you got a stopwatch? I want you to ask your dad for one next time your birthday rolls around.

All right, kid, I haven't done this in a long time so I might be a little bit rusty but I don't think I've lost the touch. A gun is as good as the man who wears it, as old Shane said. What do you mean I'm making faces? I'm concentrating, stupid. Ouch! Oh, damn! What do you think I did? My finger got caught in the stupid thing. No, I wouldn't have blown it off if it

22

had been a real gun, wise guy! O.K., ready? I didn't
say "draw" yet! No, they don't say draw in the movies,
but we're not in the movies! You sure know how to
make a guy mad.

Forget it, kid. Sure, if you want to think that you
outdrew me, go right ahead. No, no! That's O.K. I'd
rather just practice by myself, if you don't mind. Yeah,
I'll take mine home. O.K. Just once more. Now, ready?
When I say it! I was just asking you if you were ready;
I wasn't saying "ready."

Let's do this whole thing right. We face each other
and pretend we're on this dusty street—at high noon.
Now—we look at each other. Real cool. Don't laugh,
stupid! This is serious, it's a shoot-out, for God's sake!
Now! What the hell did you do? You drew out your
guns, right? You did not pull the trigger. I did. So
you're dead. Oh, forget it. I'm not playing lousy games
with a lousy kid. No, I'm not a sore loser! Go and get
me a Coke and some potato chips.

What the hell happened to the garlic-flavored ones?
If they don't have them at the A & P how about telling
your mother next time to try Grand Union? Oh, boy,
sometimes I feel if I didn't tell everybody how to do
things, the whole rotten world would fall apart.

Hey, turn it down. That's the part where nothing
much is happening. Listen, kid, we haven't had a good
man-to-man talk in a long time, right? Let me tell
you about life, kid. How're you getting along with
your parents? What do you mean "great"? You've
got troubles, Charlie. Don't you know that something

23

must be rotten? How the hell do you expect me to know? What are you getting along so well with your parents for? Just ask yourself. They don't bug you and you don't bug them. That ain't natural. You've got to be real different, from not only them, but from me too. Let me explain it to you, kid. Why is the world so lousy? Because people are always the same. Making the same dumb mistakes. Doing the same dumb things. The kids end up the same as their parents. And the way I figure it, kid, is we've got to change it by being different from anyone else.

I'll level with you, Charlie. I've been doing a lot of thinking about how it is with me—not having any real friends except for you—and being a loner and everything. It used to make me feel real weird, but just the other day I thought to myself that I might have something going for me—in being different and not wanting to be part of all the stuff that other kids my age are doing. I mean, I don't really mind anymore the way I am. Straight and square. Except for one thing. I am not real smart and I certainly don't have any ambition or stuff like that. So when I grow up I probably won't make any waves. But you could be somebody. You really could make a difference.

I'm trying to tell you that you've got to watch yourself at all times. You've got to make the right kind of kid out of yourself and that means you've got to understand about your parents, and you don't.

First of all you've got to keep your parents on their toes or else they won't know what life's all about. I mean they're over the hill—being their age and all.

You've got to be the one to bring some excitement into their lives. Like how many times a day do you get your mother excited about something? No, she isn't supposed to be playing it cool! She's a mother. She's supposed to yell. It's good for her. I'll lay it to you on the line, kid. There are just a few things that a mother's got going for her and one of them is telling her children what to do. You take that away from her and she might become real depressed. There is this one kid in my class and his mother's a boozer, and I bet she's a boozer because he's such a sweet kid—he never gave her any trouble. She never had to yell at him or anything—so she started hitting the bottle. That's how I figure it. Now, take me for instance. I really don't like to smoke, but once in a while I let my mom catch me smoking so she can yell at me.

Hey, did you see that? Did you see the Duke hit that guy? Man, can he ever smack the baddies around good!

O.K., so where were we? Make your mother happy; do something rotten once in a while. I don't know like what. Start spitting or leave a trail behind you or something to make her yell at you. No, it's not to be different. That's to be like all the other kids. In small things I want you to act like other kids, but in big important things, I want you to be different from anybody around. That's what I'm trying to get across to you, Charlie. You make a smoke screen for yourself. Make people think you're a normal kid so you get accepted, and then spring it on them. What? I don't know. I'm trying to figure it out for you because I've already loused up my chances. The thing is with me people look at me and already they're suspecting I'm some kind of a nut. I've earned me a bad reputation. But you, kid, you're just starting out. You could really get away with being a great person.

If you don't know what I'm talking to you about don't worry, because I only just started thinking about it. What bothers me is the fact that we grow up but we don't get any better, only worse. And I don't know why that is. Maybe you have the brains to figure it out. You ever notice kids younger than you—how nice and friendly and open they are, and happy? And then you ever notice kids my age—how self-conscious they are, and how phony and miserable they look most of the time? Well, what I want to know is, why is that?

I mean, just look at me. What am I doing with my life? Playing draw with you and you win. And you know what? I could have outdrawn you any day five years ago. And what are we watching? *Red River*. I've seen it a couple of dozen times and you know something? I'm not enjoying it as much as I used to. The picture's the same, but I'm not. It would be O.K. if I just said to myself, Byron, as long as you're growing up to be a moron, at least be a happy moron. But the trouble is, first of all I don't want to grow up, and second of all I don't think I'm really a moron, and third of all I am not happy.

If you won't laugh I'll tell you something. Sometimes I think I'm a genius or something. It's really funny except it isn't, if you know what I mean. Do you know what I keep doing in school? I argue with the teachers. All the time! I actually argue with them about the stuff they're teaching us. Not because I've read anything but because I'm sure I know more than they do. I'm the original smartass of the western world! And what's killing me is wondering what the hell am I really? A genius or a dummy? Cut it out, I'm not! But, hell, I'm not a moron either, and I don't want to fall somewhere in between. It's got to be one or the other.

You know something else that's weird? I want to learn everything. I mean, from the beginning. I'd like to start all over. Like, I'd really like to be your age or even younger. Because the thing is—I get this rotten feeling that I'm supposed to be moving some-where—like inside my head. But I'm not. And maybe I'm right—the damn school is to blame. Because all I do is just sit there staring out of the window and noth-ing's happening to my mind except when I start ar-guing with those damn teachers. But they don't even want to argue back!

How do you like that? I told you that I'm probably the only living mental freak and you just sit there and you're not even laughing. Turn that thing off! No, I don't want to see the end. I'm getting depressed and I want you to get upstairs and leave me alone. And on your way out, turn off the light. I just want to sit here in the dark and try to figure things out. O.K., I'll come up and tuck you in, but for Christ sake, you better start growing up, kid, or you'll end up as mixed up as I am.

Winter and Sixteen

That's real tough, kid. Oh, God, it really is tough on you. Look, kid, it isn't going to help you any now but, you know, it might be for the best. I mean, look at it this way—if they stayed together and really got to hate each other—you'd see that. You'd feel it, and you'd be much worse off. As it is, it's only a separation, see? I mean, it doesn't have to end in a divorce. Don't cry, kid. Oh, hell, yeah, do cry if you want to. Just keep wiping your nose, that's all. I mean, there is nothing worse than a little kid with snot coming out of his nose. Hey, I made you laugh!

O.K., so the way I figure it, it was coming. Remember the first time I sat for you? I mean your father was painting and not selling any of his stuff, right?

28

He probably shouldn't have given up that teaching job. Because your mother had this novel that was so damn popular and the movie sale and stuff, it must have been real tough on your old man. I bet they stayed together as long as they did because of you. You have to hand it to them. I mean, it came as a big surprise to you, right? You didn't know what was going on—and I bet plenty was—because people don't split up over nothing. So you just keep on digging your mom and your dad. Both. Yeah, don't play favorites or anything.

So how is it going to be? You'll stay with your mother? Sure, that's how it's always done. Well, look at it this way, you can visit him any time you want to. Weekends, sure! And summers too and during vacations. And maybe they'll get back together, who knows? You know what, your eyes go all pale when you're bawling. Yeah, no kidding, you look like a blind kid or something. No, I didn't mean it, really. It's just that I wish you'd stop crying. No, of course not. My parents won't get divorced because they're sort of used to each other. Yeah, some people get lived in with each other. But God, when I get married, which won't ever happen anyway, I want something better than what they've got. I don't know what. But better, that's all. I mean, Jesus, if that's all there is to life I don't want it!

What are you crying about now? No, you're not going to lose your daddy! You just wait and see; you'll have more fun with him than ever. Oh, you used to do that? Every morning you used to jump on top of him to wake him up? Hey, kid, you sure your father isn't leaving because of that? No, I was only joking. That's sort of nice, doing that to your old man. I think I remember doing that too when I was a hell of a lot younger than you. Look, kid, you've got to realize one thing, you've got to grow up, see, and you can't expect to go on jumping on your old man all your life, you know what I mean?

That's swell about him getting a studio in New York City. You can visit him any old time. And, you know, you'll get to do all sorts of things together. How the hell should I know? But I guess he'll be taking you to see the Mets and to the zoo and things like movies and plays and museums and stuff like that. In a way, I bet it will be much better for you. It will be like having two homes. You don't want to have two homes? Sure things will change. But that's how it is with life and you've got to face up to it.

What the hell do you want to worry about that for? They aren't even divorced and you're worrying about them remarrying? Maybe they'll even get back together, though I wouldn't count on that too much. You will not kill anybody! So what if your mother got some boyfriend or something. She's a pretty good-looking dame for her age, and she just might go out with some guy. You will not hate him! We'll just case him together, see? We'll do it together and before he takes her out anywhere we'll ask him what his intentions are, O.K.?

Look, I don't say they will and I don't say they won't, but if they did get a divorce that wouldn't be the end of your world. They've got a right to lead their lives and you've got a right to lead yours. You can't fall apart over that. There're ten billion kids who live through stuff like that—their parents' divorce. And the only thing I've got to say to you is you've got to start getting tough. The thing to do is not count on anybody not changing, because everybody's got to do that. No, don't even count on me!

The thing is not to get too dependent on anyone, see? That way nothing can hurt you too bad. Look at me, I've got nobody. Sure I've got you. But one day I'll leave this lousy town and then you'll be alone and you'll have to make it on your own. Same as me.

What do you want to show me your report card for? You know they depress the hell out of me. Oh, O.K., if you really want to and if it will make you feel any better. Oh, boy, here we go again. Straight A's. What are you trying to prove, Charlie? Look, kid, we've been over that. But let me spell it out for you once more. School is a phony setup. I mean, how the hell do they expect anybody to learn anything when it's all dished out the same way to everybody? They make you a sheep, and if you're a good little sheep you get straight A's as a reward. Don't you see, kid, you've got to fight it! You've got to fight the system! Why? Because that's one of the important things in life. You see something rotten, you don't join in and make it work; you make the rotten thing get fouled up.

The way I see it, for any school to be worth while you'd have one teacher for one kid. At least for a few minutes each day. So that the kid and the teacher would get to know each other. As people, for Christ sake! Because I don't really blame those teachers too much. I'd be a rotten teacher too if I were faced with a whole bunch of kids. A whole bunch of kids, all together, can drive anybody crazy.

I had this argument today. With the principal. Man, I might even get kicked out but I just couldn't take it anymore. Well, I stormed into his office and said, "How the hell can anybody figure out a way of grading 'in your opinion' questions?" He didn't get it at first, just like you. I mean, I got an F on one of those questions. And the question was: "In your opinion, what was Napoleon's greatest accomplishment?" So, what I wrote was "In my opinion Napoleon's greatest accomplishment was overcoming his lack of height." And she gave me an F for that! I said the truth and she gives me an F! If I was going to bullshit her she'd give me an A. The lousy little Frenchman, that *was* his greatest accomplishment! The principal, he said it wasn't a serious answer. Well, I don't take Napoleon seriously!

Next time you show me one of your report cards I'll puke right over it. Sure I'll show you one of mine. I'm barely squeezing past and I figure if I work hard at it I'll graduate last in my class. But the trouble with that is that it takes most of my time. Figuring out how not to exactly flunk out but to come in last.

Get off me, will ya? I've told you a thousand times I don't like you climbing on my back. Oh, you saw me

with that creep of a girl? Yeah, I bought her a Coke
but, man, was that ever a waste of money. I've never
seen anyone so stuck-up in my life—except she's pretty
well stacked. I was going to do her a favor and take
her to that ridiculous dance they're having at the Barn.
What happened? She was going with some other creep,
that's what. And, God, if I had just kept my big mouth
shut I wouldn't have been turned down by big boobs.
But it taught me something anyway. I'm not going to
be impressed by big-boobed girls and next time I get
a dumb idea about asking a girl out, I'll pick on a real
plain jane and give her the thrill of a lifetime.

Turn that thing off, will ya? They sure loused up
TV. Who the hell gave them the right to put so many
lousy programs on the air? And not one decent movie
all week long. No, I don't watch that crappy show! I'm
telling you, it stinks! TV is getting boring as all hell
and you're hooked on it. You sure were born too late,
Charlie, all the good shows are off the air now.

Hey, I met a real cool kid in the diner last night. I
was just sitting there, having some doughnuts and
coffee and this long-haired cat walks in and you should
have heard all those dummies—the truck drivers and
jokers like that. What a bunch of creeps! They can't
ever think of anything original to say about a long-
haired guy, same stuff, "Is that a girl or a boy?" and
putting him down real bad. All because of his hair.
Can you imagine, those same jokers go out to vote and
how the hell do you expect the country to survive all
those idiots who only care how people look? Sometimes I'm so ashamed for people I want to go off some-

place and live with a bunch of animals. Anyway, I began to talk with this guy—just to make him feel that there was someone in that diner that wasn't a complete jackass. He said I give off good vibrations; isn't that great?

You know something? I almost drove off with him. I don't know, maybe it's because you're around, ruining my life, but I could have driven off to California with that guy. He had this old beat-up station wagon with a whole bunch of amplifiers and things inside. His group split up and he was on his way back to San Francisco. And I could have gone with him!

Hell! Sometimes I wish I had nobody in this whole wide world who was counting on me. Like my folks —they'd die if I split. You know, I figure that it would be better to have parents who were real mean and nasty and that you could hate. Then you'd be free to do all sorts of things with your life and you wouldn't care because they wouldn't care. There was this old movie I once saw on "The Late Show." It was called *Knock on Any Door* and this guy in it, his whole philosophy of life was, live fast, die young, and have a good-looking corpse. Boy, if you weren't polluting my life and if my parents were some sort of creeps, that's what I'd like to do. Live, for Christ sake!

What are you doing? Will you cut that out? I'm happy! I'm happy because you're around! Don't bug me! I was just dreaming! Look, kid, you've got to understand that I don't mind you. I like you. You ought to know that, but like I was saying you can't ever be free if you're dependent on people. And one day we've got to figure out how we're going to cut loose from each other. Because you've got to do it. And I've got to do it. But don't cry, stupid, I'll see you through at least the fourth grade. Which I hope you flunk!

You know what I'd do if I could do anything? I'd travel all over the damn world and I'd find out about people. All kinds of things, but mostly what makes some of them real nice and kind and great and what makes others rotten human beings. And then I'd make this list. I hate lists and stuff like that, but this list of mine would be different. It will be sort of scientific but mostly it will be the kind of stuff that you can't find anyplace. See, I'd add up all the things that it takes to be a real beautiful person. That's what I don't know, stupid! That's what I'd try to find out! But the thing is, once I'm done with it it will be like a great discovery. And when I'm dead or something, kids would be studying this list of mine in schools and everybody could grow up to be real fine.

The trouble is, so far, I've only been interested in myself and it's beginning to bore the hell out of me. I mean, people are damn interesting, but who the hell is interesting around here? Nobody. So I've got to travel to discover them.

What are you talking about? Your mother couldn't adopt me, for God's sake! I don't want to be adopted by your mother! No, I wouldn't let your mother take me all over the world. Oh, that's what you were getting at. Well, kid, maybe we could. Maybe the two of us could do just that. No, you wouldn't be in my way. I'd let you make the list! And you notice things pretty well, four eyes! Sorry, I wasn't saying that like those creeps in school, but if I were you I'd try to get some other kind of glasses. Well, you look like a midget professor or something with those on. No! Don't break them—just next time you go to your eye doctor I'll come with you. Not tomorrow! You just got those glasses, for God's sake! Look, I didn't mean it. I like them! Now leave them alone before you break them and then your neck.

What would it be like? The way I'd like to travel, to tell you the honest truth, wouldn't be on some hot motorbike or anything like a sports car. I'd like to go on a horse, and sometimes on a train. That's how we'd go around the world. There must be some wide-open spaces somewhere, like in the Westerns. No, I've never been on a horse but I bet you anything I'd know how to ride.

I think we'll know a lot by just looking at people's faces. I mean there are some plastic people and there are some real people. No, not real plastic! The plastic people are the ones who are afraid of being themselves. You can sort of tell by their faces. They let other people think for them and even live for them, so we'd bypass the plastic people. But the real people, who aren't afraid of anything, they could tell us things we want to know. And we'd talk to kids before they got spoiled by being afraid to think for themselves. And we'd talk to the old people because they shouldn't have anything to lose before dying. They wouldn't bullshit us.

36

And if we went into a town that looked like the last town we'd been to we wouldn't just say, oh, it's just like the last town we've been to, because it couldn't be. We wouldn't settle for the crap they teach us about people all being the same, because they couldn't be! If they were, that'd be the end of the line for us. Because, you see, kid, in school they try to make us all the same. And God didn't do that. He made us all different.

And if there were famous places to see where we went we wouldn't even bother to see them. I mean, we wouldn't be going to see any dumb thing like Niagara Falls or the Grand Canyon. We'd be going looking for people. We'd find ourselves somebody who once dug for gold and he'd tell us about how it was in those days. And we might even find a black guy who'd been a slave, and he'd tell us about that. And we would go into the hills and hear them sing songs, and we'd go and talk to cowboys—real working cowboys. There must be some of them left around. And we would go across this country and discover whether it's still good or whether something has actually happened to it and it's rotten, like some say.

And we'd find ourselves some rivers that nobody knows about and we'd go down those rivers on a raft. And we'd find ourselves some mountains that nobody got around to naming and we'd give them names. And sometimes we'd bring gifts to people and sometimes we'd get gifts from people. And we'd learn how to live off the land by fishing and hunting and maybe even asking for things—not like begging, but just asking

37

for people to share what they've got with us. And we'd share with people. And we wouldn't stay in any place too long, but we'd leave each place with the feeling that any old time we'd like to we could come back and find old friends there. And sometimes we'd have to work; and we'd work on farms or gas stations or ranches and we would just make enough money so that we wouldn't starve.

When we're through seeing this whole country, then we could ship out to other places in the world. How would you like to go to Australia and New Zealand, and all those islands in the Pacific Ocean? Because to tell you the truth I wouldn't want to go to Europe with you right away, since you've already been there and you'd get very bossy and smart about telling me things. We should go to places where neither one of us had ever been, which won't be hard for me because I've never been anywhere.

Why don't we do it now? Oh, kid, don't you know that I've been just dreaming? Hey, don't start that again! Dreams are like that, you never know. Maybe they'll come true and maybe they won't. We'll just have to wait and see. And maybe one day, when both of us get pissed off enough about things as they are, we'll take off. I'm not promising you a thing, but who knows. One day we might just do that. One day we just might.

Fall and Seventeen

So you like her? Why do I call a car a her? I don't
know, but isn't she a beauty? She's only seven years
old and she's only got eighty thousand miles on her.
Boy, did I ever make a deal! Just guess how much I
got her for. You're way off. Four hundred and twenty-
two bucks! That's what the guy needed. I mean he
advertised it for five but came down but wouldn't
come down any lower. You want to take a spin with
me? Just dig that! Take a spin! That's what they used
to say around the turn of the century when they got
their first car. Hey, are your fingers sticky or anything?
I don't want you to mess up my interior. What do you
mean what is it? It's a Falcon, for God's sake!

Did I pass my test! Would you ask that of a master

driver? I had it all figured out before I went. I've been watching those guys taking their road tests while mom was going through inspections. The thing is, all those scared guys take it too easy, going about two miles an hour and they upset the inspectors, see? So I got it up to twenty-five which is the speed limit. Sure, he thought I was a real cool driver except he gave me a whole lecture on safety and stuff like that. I mean he even got some pictures out of his pocket. Of accidents. People smashed all over the roads and trees. Boy, were they gross!

I'm watching! What the hell are you, a backseat driver or something? Just keep your hands in your pockets. I've polished that dashboard so it would last. And don't stuff your dumb gum wrapper in my ashtray. Suppose I pick a girl up who smokes? She'd set the damn car on fire, for God's sake!

What do you want to go home for? Don't you like to drive around for a while? Boy, do those bastards charge a lot for gas. And you know what, I've got to get a job because I've got to pay my own insurance. They're a bunch of rotten thieves, those insurance people! Just because you're young they charge you double. I think it's unconstitutional. I never knew how much this whole deal of owning a car would run into. Greasing and snow tires and all sorts of stuff. But you know what, Charlie, this car really is like part yours. I used the dough I made off of you. Yeah, no kidding! Baby-sitting money!

Sure. You're the first person to get a ride in her. No,

I didn't take my mom or dad for a ride; I wanted you to be the first. Don't thank me, stupid. What are you sniffling for? You know what, kid, I think you're becoming overemotional. That's your problem. How often have I told you to play it cool? Sure like me. What are you talking about? I never get emotional! You ever see me get emotional? Forget that. Listen, now that I've got me my own car I'll play it so cool that I'll be walking around with my ass frozen off.

I've got it made now. Man, is it ever great to have a car! Why? Because what you get when you get a car is freedom, kid. And freedom, kid, is about as close to paradise as you can get. I can do things now. Like what? Are you kidding? Everything! I can get places. You out of your mind? I never went no place. You don't feel like going anywhere when you don't have a car. When did you see me ride a bike? I haven't ridden my bike in the last four years. When you get to be my age you feel dumb riding a bike. I don't know why—maybe because you're dumb at my age, I don't know. I'm not all that different from other kids my age. It's just that not being old enough to drive and not having a car really does screw your life up. You just watch me from now on. O.K., O.K., we'll go home. But doesn't she drive like a dream?

What knocking? It just needs adjusting, that's all. I got me a manual and will work on her myself. What noise, for God's sake? That's just the exhaust pipe. It's broken, that's all, but doesn't she ride like a damn Caddie? No? Your Caddie rides like a Caddie? What do

41

you want to be the rest of your life, a smartass or something?

Boy, why does your mother have to have that rock in her driveway? Just look at that! Will you just look at that! One day she's going to get sued by someone! It's not a scratch that you can't even see! It's a damn sight more than a scratch! It's a wrecked car, that what it is! Next time tell her to put a bigger rock there so that my whole fender could get smashed, for God's sake! I'll heave that damn rock wherever I please, that's what I'll do, and I don't care about her stupid reason for having it where it was; it's a real hazard, that's what it is. Boy, just don't talk to me for a couple of hours until I cool off. Oh, shut up!

i

What the hell are you crying about now? Oh, I'm sorry. So tell me about seeing your dad. How is he doing? A what? No kidding? A real sailboat! Why didn't you? So what? So he had a dame come along; so what did that have to do with you not having a great time? I mean, man, sailing must be one of the greatest things in life! Why'd you hate her? Look, kid, if your father wants to hold hands with a chick he's got a perfect right to. Divorced men can hold hands with any dame they want to. Well, you just stop hoping for that because there's not a chance in hell of them ever getting together again. Before the divorce, maybe, but not

42

now. So grow up and start accepting things as they are.

Do you figure he'd like to marry her or something? A bathrobe hanging in the bathroom doesn't mean a thing. She might not be living with him. How do you know it wasn't his bathrobe; guys are wearing queer-looking clothes nowadays. You know what, I wish you didn't notice things like that. Why do you have to keep noticing everything all the time? Little kids ought to keep their eyes closed half of the time because too much of what they see confuses them too much.

God, I keep forgetting that you're a little kid and you're becoming insecure as all hell. Man, what happened to you? You used to be so damn happy! That's what's so rotten about divorces, the way it mixes up the kids. But hell, Charlie, you're better than that. Don't let things get you down. Sure I'll see you. I don't know exactly when. But I'll try to make it before Saturday. I hate to promise things. O.K., I promise.

ii

So what was so damn important that I had to drop everything and rush over? What's the matter with you? You look awful. When did you start stammering, for God's sake? If it doesn't matter now, how come it was so damn important five minutes ago? O.K., I'll forget it, since I didn't even know what the hell it was all about.

43

No, I don't want to see your cruddy report card; I saw one last month and I told you . . . Oh, really? How come? How come you're shaping up? An *F* in gym? What the hell do you mean you stay in the can during gym? What for? What did you do to deserve a *B* minus in math? Oh, great! Don't worry, kid, you're doing O.K., especially with that *D* in English.

What do you mean you did it for me? I don't want you to do anything for me! I want you to do things like that for yourself. Hey, is that what you wanted to tell me? I thought you had something else on your mind besides your grades. O.K., kid, I've got to go now. Do I have to tell you everything? As a matter of fact, I'm going to see about a job. It's a sort of a dream job so keep your fingers crossed, will ya? What are you crying about now? Look, I haven't got time. Tell me later. Yeah, if I get it I'll come over and tell you about it. You know I hate to promise you things. O.K., O.K., I promise.

iii

I got it! I got the job! It's the greatest. Now, listen, kid, if you wanted to make some money and at the same time learn about what life's all about, where would you go? What do I mean? You know how I am, the way I want to learn about things. O.K., so listen! I figure that the only way to learn is from another human being, not some cruddy books, right? So who could be better than old people, the ones who are ready to croak? They must have a hell of a lot of experiences and wisdom, right? And who is tapping all that wisdom? Nobody! Except now I will! Not only that, I'll be paid to do it. That's what I'm trying to tell you. I've got me a job at an old people's home!

Oh, man, was it ever pure luck! I never even read the Paterson paper, but yesterday I took a look at their classified section, and there it was: "Wanted, a young person willing and able to entertain elderly people. Duties will include reading and conversing. Apply, Sunnyfield Home for the Aged." So I went over there and got it! Two-fifty an hour! Every day from three thirty to six thirty, including Saturdays and Sundays. Isn't that great?

She can get someone else. Oh, come on, Charlie, if I work there I can't baby-sit for you. Sure, Saturday nights, maybe I could, but not always. I mean, I'm not going to plan to spend every damn Saturday night sitting for you. All right, do you want to hear about it or are you going to bawl?

Hey, you got any diet soft drinks? No, I don't drink Cokes anymore. Since yesterday. Because of my zits, for God's sake! Just look at them. I can't even shave without busting them all open and bleeding like a pig. Sure I shave! Almost every day, can't you tell? Oh, come off it! Just tell your mom to get me some of that diet stuff, will ya? I'd go to a skin doctor if only I had the dough, but, man, am I ever broke! I had to get some new spark plugs and the guy at the garage told me that if I don't reline the brakes I'll kill myself.

What do you want to do that for? Keep your lousy piggy-bank money! You really want to make me a loan of it? How much you got there? Don't break it! Oh, O.K. I'll get you another pig—for Christmas maybe. Yeah, that ought to do it. Sure I'll use it for my brakes, what do you think I'd use it for? Hey, thanks, kid. You know what, kid, you're a real pal.

So, listen! Is Sunnyfield a great sort of a place! It's in the middle of a lousy section of Paterson, but once it did face a field, or that's what Mrs. Pease told me. She's the dame that runs the place, looks exactly like Margaret Dumont. Haven't you been watching the Marx brothers festival on Channel Five like I told you to? So how can you ask? Yeah, sure, the dame that Groucho's always after, that's Margaret Dumont. And listen, they have this great room there—with a big piano and a harp—and, God, when I was talking to Mrs. Pease I swear I thought Harpo, Groucho, and Chico would barge in any minute. But instead, these queer sisters did. They're twins and they're about a hundred years old, real funny looking in these old clothes. Hey, you ever seen *What Ever Happened to Baby Jane?* Well, anyway, they look like Bette Davis did in that movie. I swear they did, and they're senile, right out of their minds, and they were talking in this baby talk. Boy, was that weird. I thought I was in a nut house or something.

You wouldn't believe it, this place. It was a private

mansion once, owned by these two Polish brothers, and they were boozers or something because this dame showed me a pamphlet from Prohibition days that claimed this place was a secret refuge for elderly boozers. But she said that it wasn't so at all, that it wasn't secret at all. When the two brothers went sort of senile they opened up their house to other old guys who liked boozing. Anyway, she said the place has like a trust fund and gets money for having a bum living there. And if there isn't a bum around for a week for one reason or another they'd lose a whole bunch of money, so tomorrow I'm supposed to go looking for a bum with her. Yeah, no kidding! Well, the last bum they had ran away, climbing down this tree they've got near the house. She doesn't know why. I guess maybe a bum would get nervous in a grand place like that. Anyway, tomorrow, if she doesn't find a bum by then—and she's been calling places looking for one—we've got to go down to New York and get us one. Hell, I don't know how! She might have to kidnap somebody or something.

She's a little nutty, too, that dame, Mrs. Pease. She keeps talking about making this Sunnyfield place a cultural center of the world or something and from what I saw of the people there they don't look to me like no cultural geniuses or anything, they just look pretty old. Boy, did I have to bullshit her about how culturally inclined I was and everything. I mean she really digs art and theater and music and stuff like that. But the way I figure, all those old people would rather hang around in this room where there's a big color TV set.

Sure, I'll tell you. I'll call you tomorrow. Yeah, I've got to go now, and, hey, thanks for the loan. No, kid, I'm not going to. I told you a couple of hundred times that guys don't kiss guys. Why don't you ask your mother to kiss you once in a while or get yourself a girl? You kidding? Oh, yeah. She did? What kind of a guy? Why do you say you hate him? What's he do? Look, kid, everybody who lives in Hollywood calls everybody darling. It doesn't mean a thing. Don't worry about it. If he's the director that's all he came over for, to talk things over with her. Look, kid, you've got to realize that one day your mom is going to meet some guy and maybe want to marry him. That's normal. No, you can't hate her for that! Oh, man, did they really? They signed them up to play in your mother's movie? Wait till I tell my mom; she's crazy about them! She's crazier about those two than any other movie stars in the world.

Look, kid, I haven't got time to stick around tonight. But I'll call you tomorrow. Yeah, I promise. O.K., I'll drive over. Just stop bugging me, will ya? I mean, I'm going to be busy as hell with my job and stuff. What do you mean you cried yourself to sleep last night? Stupid, you ought to be a happy kid. People who are eight years old shouldn't have anything to cry about. Listen, promise me you'll never cry yourself to sleep again as long as you live. O.K., so if you feel like crying just call me and I'll come over and we'll talk or something. I've got to go now.

The reason I couldn't come over is that I couldn't. I know you called. My mother told me. Sure I promised, but didn't you have anyone break a promise before? I had to go out with this girl. I mean I had this great chance to . . . what the hell am I telling you this for? I told your mother I couldn't sit for you last Saturday night, didn't she tell you? Sure, I went out with the same girl again. If you were older I'd tell you. And the thing is I'd like to go out with her tonight, too. No! It's just that . . . hell! I'm not going to talk sex to a little kid.

What do you want to run away from home for? You're crazy! Don't do anything stupid like that. You're all packed? Where the hell do you think you'd go? A stupid kid like you if he's going to run away's got to figure these things out. What's so terrible? You can't talk on the phone! Well, kid, you better learn because half of everything that's said is said on the damn phone.

Look, kid, once in a while I might have to go out. Sure, with a girl! I'm a big boy! I don't hate all girls anymore. No, she's not that special—except she is for what I need. Look, kid, you've got your life to lead and I've got mine. So don't bug me!

Listen! You unpack your stuff. If you don't, I'll have to come over and that will ruin my chance for . . . Hell! Don't I have any right to privacy! Look, if you're going to be a regular pain in the ass I'll just have to ease you out of my life. Damn it! Don't cry, for God's sake! One thing I can't stand is you crying. You didn't keep your promise either! I told you, you can't cry at night. Not in the day either! You stop crying or I'll never see you again and that's a promise. What do you mean I don't keep promises anyway? Just that one time I didn't, that's all. Oh, shit! I told you I will! I'll be there in half an hour and what I want you to do is just unpack your stuff, turn the TV on, and sit and wait for me. And don't think about anything. Because I'm your brain, that's why!

V

All right, I'll give you about two minutes to explain that to me. What makes you think nobody gives a damn about you? So, big deal! Going out to dinner two nights in a row! Well, make up your mind, what is it that you don't like—your baby-sitter called Mary-Ann, or your mother going out with this guy?

Hey, what's this stuff you packed in that damn suitcase? What the hell do you want with a teddy bear? I don't care how long you had it! You want to be a smartass and run away from home, you run away without that teddy bear. Oh, man, I'm telling you, you're about to make medical history. Senile at the age of eight!

I'm listening to you and the reason I'm unpacking your suitcase is that you're not going anywhere. No, my family won't adopt you! You've got a perfectly good mother and father. Their being divorced has nothing to do with that.

Now, you just sit there and listen to me. You want to be a loser all your life? You want to pack up and run away every time you've got a problem? Is that what you want to do with your life? Oh, so you want to be dead. Great! Why don't you wait until Christmas and ask Santa Claus for a neat little coffin? Hell! I am mad! You know, what you need is a belt in the mouth! You go on to the bathroom, blow your stupid nose, wash your eyes, and come back smiling or you lose the best friend you'll ever have.

Can't you smile better than that? You still want to be an astronaut? Because I heard this great joke about two Polish astronauts. You don't want to hear it, O.K., you're not going to hear it. You know what your problem is? You're thinking of yourself too damn much. All right, if you want to talk, I'll let you talk.

So you didn't see your daddy for two whole weeks. It doesn't mean he forgot you or that he doesn't want to see you. He's probably busy. Sure! I'm busy too. What are you going to do, get jealous of my job? How would it be if we all gave up everything we're doing and just stayed with you? Yeah, all the time. We'd go to school with you and everything. You know what would happen? Your mother, your father, and I, we'd flunk third grade, that's what. We couldn't learn the new math, that's why. And you'd go on to the fourth grade alone.

I know that. So what should you do? You should

care for more than just three lousy people. As a matter of fact, at your age, kid, even I had a whole bunch of friends. And I don't remember ever being depressed at your age, kid. I mean, what the hell's going to happen to you if you can get depressed already? By the time it's really depressing, at about eleven, you'll have run out of depression, for Christ sake.

You don't want to be like me! You can't! You've got to be different; you've got to be your own man, kid. What can I tell you? You've got to get out of the funk you're in. Anything. Start a stamp collection or something, for God's sake. And let her lead her own life. She wants to go out, let her go out. But I can't sit with you when I work at Sunnyfield!

Yeah, we've got us a bum. We picked him up in New York City. Do you want to hear about it? O.K., I'll tell you about him and all the stuff that happened at Sunnyfield some other time. Do you want to shoot some pool? How about a ride? Well, what the hell do you want to do? You know what I'm missing right this minute? Yeah, and does this chick really put out! Oh, hell, sex is too important to screw around with. Remind me in about ten years to tell you all the great wisdom I've acquired in the last couple of days.

You want to be alone? You really want me to go now? Look, Charlie, I don't care about that girl. I'd rather be with you. No, I'm not kidding. I figure I'd just as soon wait around until I meet somebody I really like. No, I don't like her! Are you kidding? You and I are pals. For life.

You going to be O.K.? You're sure now? You know what, you look like a drowned puppy or something. Listen, kid, everything's going to be all right. In a couple of days you won't even remember what was bugging you. So start getting undepressed. I can stick around. All night if you want me to. I really mean it. You sure you'd rather be alone?

So, what's the big deal? I can give you a hug if I feel like giving you a hug. See you around, Charlie. Tomorrow. I'll come by tomorrow right after Sunny-field. I've got an idea! Why don't you invite me for one of your fancy dinners? Well, we could cook it ourselves. So, I'll send Mary-Ann home when I get here. Hey, kid! Keep your chin up.

vi

Oh, my God, no! How is he? When did it happen? For Christ sake, why do you keep sleeping pills around? Is he going to be O.K.? What hospital? Can I see him? Why the hell not? I want to see him! Screw the doctor. Look, I swear a lot, that's a shitty habit I've got and I don't see why the hell we should be talking about my swearing at a time like this.

Didn't you notice it? For about a couple of weeks. And last night he was more depressed than ever. I just couldn't cheer him up or anything. He wanted to be alone. God, things just piled up on him! How the hell is a little kid of eight supposed to cope with things like divorce? It was my fault too. I broke a promise to him. And getting the job . . . Sure. I mean how the hell could you not notice? I don't mean to upset you, but damn it, you're going out all the time and his father's too busy even to see him! But you're not in a hospital! He is!

O.K. if he can't have visitors but, God, you better tell me where he's at because I want to call him. How come? Well, can't I just call the damn hospital to find out how he's doing? Oh, the Valley Hospital. He did? The first thing he said was my name? Jesus! I really dig your son. I mean, he's my only friend.

What kind of a boarding school? If your brother is a psychiatrist there, doesn't that make it some kind of a nut house? Look, maybe he could stay with me instead. I mean, live at my house. I know you know what would be best for him, except does he know? Because there are a hell of a lot of little kids around who sure as hell are unhappy doing what's good for them. And a little kid shouldn't be unhappy.

When you see him thank him for making you call me, and tell him that he's a stupid jackass and he better get well soon or I'll beat his brains out. No. You better just tell him that . . . Oh, hell, don't tell him anything.

You think he'll be out inside of a week? Why couldn't I see him before you take him to that school? Hospital rules! Well, look, what room is he in? I just want to call the hospital and ask them how he's doing. Thanks. Wait! Don't worry about your kid. He's the greatest.

Pssst! Psst! Hey, Charlie! Shhh! I can't get this shitty window open any wider. What the hell did you think, that some stupid hospital rules would stop me? How're you doing, pal? No, I don't feel like giving you hell. Man, you look like some half-assed angel in that hospital nightgown. I've been around here since seven trying to get in. No, they don't let anyone in except family and stuff. It's way past visiting hours. Hey, you know what, you look pretty great. Did I wake you? No, my neck isn't going to be that sore. I got to lean this way or else you won't hear me through this damn glass. I'm holding on. This ledge here is pretty wide you know. Don't worry, kid, even if I fall I won't break my damn neck. It's only the second floor. I got up the fire escape and across the window ledges. Sure I was careful. Don't strain yourself; there's a catch or something on that window. I already tried it. So, tell me something I don't know.

Yeah, your mom told me. Do you mind going there? You know what, I've been thinking about that and I also talked it over with my parents. Now, listen, kid. If you don't like it there or anything bugs you, all you need to do is call me up. Call collect, see? Somebody's always home. Mom, that is. The moment you call, see, and tell us you want to come and live with us, we'll come and get you. Connecticut isn't that far or anything; we'll be there in a couple of hours and get

55

you. Sure I can get you out of that place even if they've got bars all over the place. Didn't I get in here?

Yeah, and look, kid, I've asked around. It's a good school. And after all you've got an uncle there, so he can sort of introduce you to all the guys and stuff. And it might not be bad at all, you know. I mean you being so bright and everything, you ought to do real good there.

You didn't have to say it, kid. I know you're sorry, but the way I look at it, everybody's entitled to act like a jackass sometimes. It's just that if you keep on acting like a jackass, doing the same dumb things, then you're in trouble. I know you won't pull a stunt like that again. Because we're going to be friends for a hell of a long time. I figure when you're about fifty and a big shot, maybe even President or something, you'll have me around. Just for laughs.

You know what I've been thinking? If we ever go traveling together let's go in a balloon. Yeah, one of those big things with a basket underneath. Wouldn't that be great? Then we could just go wherever the wind blows us. And we could have our names painted outside so people would know who we were and could call us by our first names. And then I thought we could, right underneath our names, have something printed like "Searchers for neat people," or something crazy like that. And we'd drop on people from the sky, like, and little kids would go wild over us. And we'd always say that we were checking up on little kids and how they're growing up. And we'd tell their parents to be nice and kind to them because if they weren't we'd come back and beat the hell out of them, because kids should be happy.

I better get going now. I know you're going to that school tomorrow and I want you to know I'll really miss you. Look, what I intend to do is write you every day but that probably wouldn't work out. Sometimes I'd get too busy or there'd be nothing to say, so I better not promise you that. But I'll write you as often as I've got something to say to you. And you write me whenever you feel like it and call me up, collect, any time at all. And you know what, I was wrong about playing it cool all the time. You don't have to. After your mother called I went to my room and cried for a couple of hours and that wasn't a cool thing to do but I felt like it and if there wasn't this cruddy glass between us I'd kiss you and wouldn't feel ashamed or anything.

Look, Charlie, don't let anything get you down and don't ever feel you're alone in the world or anything because you've got me. And it's O.K. for us to need and love each other; there's not a damn thing wrong with that. So, bye, kid, and keep your chin up.

Thursday night

Dear Charlie,

I just got home from the hospital after saying goodbye to you but I thought I'd write you so you'll have a letter waiting for you when you get to that school. Speaking of school, I got called into the principal's office yesterday for skipping a few classes and he gave me this big lecture about frittering my life away. Man, is he ever wrong! I've skipped school to be at Sunnyfield where I'm really learning things. At that lousy school all I've learned is that you're better off not thinking for yourself. Just memorize a whole bunch of stuff from some lousy textbook, which as far as I'm concerned are written by idiots anyway, and you've got an *A* in education. I figure, by the time you're ready to graduate from high school either all the bright kids will be dropping out or the system will change. And Hortense Meister agrees with me on that, and she's taught school for 40 years.

She and Mr. Canali are the greatest people at Sunnyfield. There are some who are pretty cruddy, especially the four old ladies,

[2]

Goodlet, Appleton, Odman and Rice. God, they're going to croak without ever finding out what life's all about. Like I asked them what their husbands had been like and each one of them told me that they were real great because they were "good providers" and left them some insurance money and stuff like that. And when I asked them about their kids, all they were saying was how well they married and how much their houses are worth. It's depressing as hell seeing those four. I bet not one of them has thought about anything important in sixty years.

There are others, like Bill Price, who is black and used to be a dancer in vaudeville, except he was in an accident and had both legs amputated. He's real nice but he'd rather talk to Donna Straka, who used to be an opera singer. She's a pretty funny lady, always telling jokes and driving the nurses who don't have any sense of humor out of their skulls. But her voice is really gone and it drives me out of my mind hearing her practice her scales.

I haven't seen too much of Leonard Ross, the bum we picked up in New York. He's been just staying in his room boozing, but

when I went there he said that next week
he'll get off the bottle and rap with me.
There is also old Engebert Humdinger but
he hasn't spoken to me yet. He never talks
to anyone, not because he can't talk or anything but he's pretty "cantankerous"
as Mrs. Pease says. He's a philosopher. Back
in the twenties or thirties he was a pretty
famous writer or that's what Mrs. Pease
told me. But he hasn't written anything in
about thirty years. That doesn't faze Mrs.
Pease any. She keeps supplying him with
typewriter paper. What he does with the
paper is make airplanes which he sails out
of his window. Yesterday I went in with Mrs.
Pease to see him and it was real funny.
She said to him, "Now, Mr. Humdinger,
how are the creative juices today?" And he
gave this Bronx cheer and got spit all over
himself because his dentures are real badly
fitted. Mrs. Pease actually thinks he'll write
a book and dedicate it to her. She's a real
nut. She even thinks that those two senile
Schneider sisters will become "culturally
oriented" and will start painting like Grandma
Moses, whoever she was.

Yesterday I tried to get a discussion started

[4]

on "The Importance of the Moon Landings in Our Lives," which was something Mrs. Pease dreamed up. It didn't get off the ground, but Donna Straka gave us a couple of rousing choruses of this corny song, "Moon over Miami." The thing is I'm not really earning my money because most of the time I just talk with Mrs. Meister and Mr. Canali and I should be paying them. I better leave telling you about them for my next letter because I promised dad to take down the window screens and it's eleven at night. He just woke up from in front of the TV and is yelling at me to get my ass out of my room. I bet what will happen is some hot-shot cop will think I'm a burglar and shoot me while I'm fooling around with those damn screens in total darkness.

I miss you real bad, worse than I thought I would. And I want to tell you that we've got a nice thing going, and whatever else happens we're friends for life. So how about writing me? And keep your chin up,

Byron

Tuesday

Dear Charlie,

Last night I drove by your house. I was going
to go in and ask your mother how you made
it over to the school and what it's like.
She was alone in the living room and I could
see her reading through the window. I don't
know why I didn't go in but I didn't. If I
don't get a letter from you by Thursday I'll
call you up and my old man will flip because he hates to fork his dough over to the
phone company. He thinks the phone and
electric companies are real blood suckers.
Last night, he was dozing in front of the
TV, like usual, and suddenly he wakes up
and says to me, "Byron, you know what I want
you to do?" I said, "I took them down, remember?" thinking he meant the screens,
but he didn't. "I want you to become a
lawyer so you can argue my case against the
phone and electric companies." He's a crazy
guy, my old man.

I was going to tell you some more about
Hortense Meister and old Canali. Hortense
is 72 years old but she's about the most intelligent person I know and that's real weird

because she's been a teacher all her life and I thought all teachers had to be dumb. The great thing about her is the way she doesn't bullshit herself about anything. She doesn't like being old. When she was a little kid she lived with her grandparents and they went senile on her. She told me how scared she used to get because they'd confuse her with her mother, who was dead. She told me about how it is, getting old, how it comes suddenly after some little unimportant thing, like dropping something or slipping. And then you lose confidence in yourself. She said, "The curvature of dying begins, the perpendicular fall." She says one day you're young, or at least you're not worried about being old, and the next day you're practically ready for the grave.

She helped me understand a lot about those four cruddy old ladies, Appleton, Goodlet, Rice, and Odman. She calls them "linebackers of life" (she knows a lot about football!) She said they stop their thinking at the point when it can get dangerous, where it can matter, because they aren't equipped to wonder about the state of their souls.

[3]

I asked her if she thinks they ever give death
a thought and she said probably not, and
anyway you can't think about death, it's
like not being able to look into the sun. But
if you live right death is nothing much to
think about. She says we practice dying every
time we go to sleep.

I sure was wrong when I thought that
when you're old and about to croak you
could have nothing to lose and could be
really great. She says that isn't the way it
works. When you get old all your habits are
more visible. Like if you've been selfish all
your life you'll be real self-centered, and if
you've been nasty, you'll really be a shit.
I don't think it should be like that, but she
says it is, because you can't change just because
you're about to die, you've got to keep on
changing while you live.

They talk a lot about the weather over
at Sunnyfield because it's like the most important thing in their lives, what kind of day
it will be tomorrow. But Hortense says it's
a natural thing to do. Nobody can do a
damn thing about the weather anyway, so
they talk about it more, and that way they

[4]

don't get too depressed about all the other things they can't do a damn about.

When I asked how come the Schneider sisters are always going back to their childhoods, she said a lot of old people do that. They might not remember what happened yesterday but they sure as hell remember everything that happened when they were eight. Because childhood is the only time when you're not responsible for anything that happens. Old people are afraid of remembering all the things they were responsible for, so they go back to when they were kids and couldn't be blamed for anything. But also, she says, it's just nice to think about childhood.

As far as she's concerned the biggest problem about being old is "holding on to a certain dignity." When you're old people treat you as if you were simple-minded, and they don't even let you die in a dignified way. They keep poking you around, sticking stuff into you and making you keep on breathing when you'd just as soon not. And by then you're usually too sick and too weak to tell them to go to hell. What she'd like to do, when her time comes to die, is be able to walk somewhere, like some hill or a field, and die alone there.

The reason she came to Sunnyfield is that a few months ago some punk kid broke into her apartment and held a knife to her. He didn't hurt her or take anything. She even gave him a lecture about what a punk thing he was doing. But now she's afraid of living alone. It made her real mad, being afraid. So she checked into Sunnyfield as a sort of a punishment. She thought she'd hate it there so much she'd go back to living alone and wouldn't be afraid. But she doesn't hate it there. She loves life but that punk really ruined part of it for her.

Mr. Canali isn't like her. He came to Sunnyfield to die. He told me that. He said that he's got nothing to live for now that his wife is dead. He really loved her which surprises me because they were married over thirty years and I didn't think anybody could really love the same person all that long. And she died because of a stupid punk kid. He was someone Mrs. Canali loved as much as her husband loved her. They couldn't have children and they took this kid in after his house and everybody in it was burned.

They lived on this estate where Mr. Canali was a gardener and they always had the neighborhood kids drop in on them, feeding them and helping them and worrying about them. But this kid they took in was real rotten. He was pushing speed and even heroin but the Canalis didn't know about that. One day he stole a whole bunch of stuff, jewelry and silver from the people the Canalis worked for. And he brought all that junk into their house and then called the police and told them that the Canalis stole it all. The police didn't believe him, but then this kid told Mrs. Canali that he hated her and did it to hurt her. He was just a real sick kid but she loved him all the same. After that Mrs. Canali just didn't want to do anything or eat anything and she just wasted away and died.

If I were Mr. Canali I know what I'd have done to that bastard. But he doesn't hate the kid. He just says, "she loved him."

I sometimes think, talking to the two of them, that I have a hell of a long way to go

[7]

to be a kind human being and that's what
Hortense Meister says life is all about, being
kind to each other. Anyway, when you come
back for Thanksgiving I will take you up
to Sunnyfield because they want to meet
you. I told them about you and now I've told
you a few things about them.

So, how about writing your pal?

Love,

Byron

Operator, you better make that person-to-person to Charlemagne Nordstrom. You want me to spell it? Can't you just pronounce it? Oh, boy, my father sure is right about your company. Look, all I want is to make a person-to-person call, do you mind? Why do you have to hassle me? I've got enough problems. Yeah, just ask for Charlemagne Nordstrom; he's a student there. It's a school, like S–C–H–double-O–L. I'm not trying to be smart, operator. I was born that way.

Well, operator, why don't you ask them why he can't come to the phone? Can he call me back— actually this is an emergency—can you ask whether Charlemagne can get out of chapel to talk to me? I'm not allowed to say what kind; it's more like a personal emergency. Well, I'll wait. What do you mean I can't wait for long? I've got all the time in the world to wait if I want to wait. Oh, I see. Well, why don't you wait until my time is up and then tell me. O.K.? Oh, boy!

Oh, hi, dad. I'll be off in a minute. Hey, do you mind closing that door; it's a personal call. No, not a girl. That's O.K., dad, don't worry about it. I'll dig girls one of these days and besides I know about them and the flowers and the bees and the whole deal. The door, dad? Yeah, I promise, a couple of minutes, that's all.

Hallo, operator? Oh, hi! O.K., operator, you do your job, but it's him, the guy I want to talk to. Now will you buzz off? Hey, Charlie, what's the matter with you? Can't you write? What the hell do you want me to worry about you for? Yeah, I'm calling you to tell you off, that's why I'm calling. How you been? How come you sound so . . . well, you sound different, that's all. You sure you're O.K.? Did you make any friends yet? Yeah . . . ? Why does he stutter? Oh! Hey is there something the matter with every kid out there? What do you mean emotionally disturbed? You're not emotionally disturbed! Don't let some jackasses tell you you are! You're a normal kid who just got screwed up by the people around you, that's all. What the hell were you doing in chapel? Glee club? Well, do you like to sing? No, I'm not saying don't sing except it's probably a waste of time. No, kid, don't listen to me, I don't want to louse you up. Yeah? You got the letter. It was a pretty stupid letter and too long for you to read, right? Oh, you did read it several times? Hey why can't you come home for Thanksgiving? Well, how is that uncle of yours? Do you like him? That's good. Well, you'll be here for Christmas, right? Hey, you sure they don't keep you prisoner there? Look, I can bust you out of there anytime you say you want to be busted out. How come you sound so independent? Well, that's good, but, Jesus, I just didn't want you to change that much. What do you mean self-sufficient; what are you using that kind of big word on me for? Oh, don't tell me! Look, I don't give a damn what your uncle Dr. Freud has to say. I'm just your friend and all I wanted to say is that I miss you and I hope you miss me too. No, I'm not mad! Why the hell should I be mad? Look, kid, I better hang up now or my dad will hit the roof. Yeah, I'll write you more about Sunnyfield, but how about you writing me? I don't give a damn what your uncle says about anything; he doesn't have any right to interfere in our friendship. So I give you permission to write me and you better not get brainwashed in that lousy school or you'll lose all your charm, kid, and without that what have you got going for you? Hey, it's nice to hear you laugh. It's like old times. Man, I sure miss sitting for you. Hell, I'll see you at Christmas. And don't let them get you down. Bye.

Monday

Dear Charlie,

It's really nice, you writing me for a change, but what the hell did you say to me? You said, "My uncle thinks I'm adjusting very well." First of all I don't give much of a damn about what your uncle thinks. Second of all what the hell are you supposed to be adjusting so damn well to? The lousy school sounds as if it's full of problem kids and you're no problem kid. And third what's with the big words like "adjusting." I mean, man, we're old friends and if anything's bugging you, like I think it is, you ought to write me a straight letter and tell me.

I was going to write you all about old Leonard Ross, who's the bum at Sunnyfield, but your letter got me so mad I'm going to drive up and see you. Next Saturday, before I have to go to Sunnyfield I'm coming over to case that joint and if we have time I'll tell you about all sorts of stuff. So, hold your breath until I come.

Love,

Byron

Hey, Charlie! Man, you must have grown two whole inches! You look great, kid. Cut it out, I don't. I look like hell; my face's breaking out again. That's why I'm growing these weird sideburns, between the two of them they cover four-and-a-half zits. Man, was it a hassle getting to see you! They wanted me to wait until ten o'clock and I told this lady I was being inducted into the army at noon. God, I hate lying, but those damn rules people make force you to.

Yeah, let's take a walk. This sure is a nice looking place. Level with me, will ya, Charlie? Do you like it here or do you hate it? What do you mean best for you? You wouldn't know what's best for you. That uncle of yours—he could be wrong, you know. Sure your mother misses you. She called last night and I told her I was coming to see you. She's coming tomorrow. How about answering my question? What do you mean, it's not bad? It's either great or rotten; which is it? So, O.K., leave it at that. But it's not bad isn't a good enough answer for me, that's all.

What's that? It sure is a great looking wallet. You made it? No kidding! Deerskin! Hey, thanks, I sure can use it; mine's falling all apart. I should have brought you something. Oh, sure, I'll tell you all about him. He's a real fantastic person, Leonard Ross is. You know what I like best about him? There is no way in the world that I can bullshit him about anything. He knows when I do and he puts me down real good

73

every time. The thing is I can't help arguing with him all the time because he thinks there is nothing rotten in this world that can't get a laugh and I keep telling him that there is hardly anything to laugh about.

Oh, sure, he drinks! He's a boozer, you might say. But the thing is, when he was about my age he promised himself that if he was still alive by sixty he was going to become a bum. He had a real fabulous life. He's been a high-wire acrobat in a circus, a motorcycle and car racer, a pool hustler, a foreign legionnaire, and a stunt pilot. And a lion tamer and a big game hunter in Africa. Well, he says so! Sure I believe him! He's a lot like Mrs. Meister because he is pissed off at being old too. Yesterday the two of them were talking about what a lousy deal it is to get old when you aren't ready for it and she quoted this guy called Diogenes who said: "Old age is the harbor of all ills." And old Ross, he said, "We didn't drop anchor there. We floundered."

How do you like this guy; I asked him if I could call him Leonard or Lenny and he said, "No, but you can call me Mr. Ross." He's like my big influence but he refuses to hand me answers on a platter. I mean, every time I ask him something he answers with a question. Like a couple of days ago I asked him if he knew what shape the world was in and he says, "Round, isn't it?" I mean, sometimes he just doesn't want to get serious with me. I accused him of copping out by being on the bum, and he says, "Copping out on what?" "On being engaged, you know, committed," I said.

And he said, "Got engaged three times and committed once, to Bellevue."

Let's sit down here, kid. And now I want you to tell me how it is with you. What kind of nightmares? When? Did you ever sleepwalk before? Why didn't you tell your uncle? That's his job, for Christ sake, to worry about you! I want to see him. Well, can't I go to his house or something? Of course I wouldn't! But you could get hurt sleepwalking. Don't be stupid; nobody'd think you did it on purpose! You know what? The way I figure it you're so damn worried about everything that at night instead of sleeping you're having nightmares and you sleepwalk. Look, kid, it's not your job to be worried about anything.

Suppose I talk to your mother. About you, for God's sake! What do you think I'd want to talk to her about? You don't want her to worry? You sure are a weird kid. I told you, she's got to worry. Just being a mother she's got to worry! Hell, I won't worry her; I'll just tell her that she ought to get you home. Well, that's O.K., she can go to Hollywood. What's to stop her getting a maid or somebody? And I'd stay with you. Or you can come and stay at my house. Because I don't think this place is good for you, that's why. I mean, God, you've got a home! You're too young to be in some lousy boarding school sleepwalking all over the place. I don't give a damn about other kids! O.K., so tell me, if I talked her into taking you away from here, would you like it? Don't slobber all over me! Hey, cut it out! You sure didn't change, Charlie!

That's great! Now I know how you feel. The thing was, I wasn't certain. I thought maybe you liked it here. I thought you might not even want to go back home. Yeah, leave it all to me. Inside of two weeks you'll be home.

x

Hallo, Mrs. Nordstrom? Yeah, I was there, just got back. Sure he looks all right and that place is some nice place. But the thing is he shouldn't be there. Well, for one thing, your kid is only eight years old. A little kid that young shouldn't be away from home. Sure, he's grown up for his age and everything, but what the hell, excuse me, but that school's full of problem kids and Charlemagne's only problem right now is that he wants to be home instead of making wallets like some camper or prisoner or something. Of course he didn't tell you. Mostly because he feels that you're probably happy to have him out from under your feet.

I know. He told me about you having to go to Hollywood. But you'll only be away for a couple of weeks, right? I figure he could stay over at my house or I could stay over at his. That's all right about the job. It's not really that much of a job. Oh, sure I love it, but for a couple of weeks I could stay away, or even take Charlemagne with me when I go. Well, I figure if you wait until after you come back it might be too late. I wasn't going to tell you this but he's been having nightmares. Yeah, pretty bad ones. And worse than that. He's been sleepwalking. And he's afraid of getting hurt. I don't know why he didn't tell you, except he doesn't want to worry you.

Oh, that'd be great! If you got a maid you wouldn't have to worry about our lousing up your house or anything. That's really nice of you, Mrs. Nordstrom. No. I wasn't that sure you'd understand. Next weekend would be perfect! One more week out there won't hurt him. Sure. I'd love to drive up with you to get him. He sure will be happy to be back home. We both will. I missed him real bad too. Well, give him my love and be sure to tell him about what you've decided. And thanks. Thanks a million.

xi

Would you like me to drive? Sure! It's not every day that I get to drive a Cadillac. This sure drives differently from my wreck of a Falcon. Would you like your air-conditioning on? Yeah, I guess it is too cold for that. How about the heater then? Oops. Well, now I know where the wipers and the lighter are. That sure is some dashboard you've got.

You read about Mr. Humdinger? What did the *Times* say? Was that his best-known book? No, I've never read anything he's written but I intend to now. You didn't see it happen on television? Oh, sure, I was there! I was sort of part of what happened. God, that was about the greatest shock of my life, actually. I don't think I'll ever forget it as long as I live.

Well, the thing was, he didn't have much use for anyone at Sunnyfield and I only got to know him a couple of days before it happened. On Monday he wanted me to come up to his room and he said to me, "I want to get on TV," he said. "Get me on TV." I didn't understand right away. For an insane moment there I thought that the old guy wanted to *sit* on a television set. I mean, there's all kinds out there at Sunnyfield and some of them are pretty senile. But then he said, "I want to be interviewed. Eighty-ninth birthday. This Wednesday. You arrange it for me." Actually I didn't arrange anything myself. Mrs. Pease, who manages Sunnyfield, did.

Anyway, when the television crew arrived at Sunnyfield on Wednesday it was pretty much of a madhouse with everybody trying to get into the act. I skipped school because Mr. Humdinger asked me to be with him. God! I didn't suspect anything and I was with him all that day. He was in a real good mood for a change. At one point he said to me, "God invented Man because He likes stories. And He invented dying because He likes His stories to have an ending. And sometimes He likes His stories to be like jokes. Sometimes He likes funny endings."

All day he kept trying to remember those old sayings. I helped him with a couple of them—the two he used first. He had twenty-four all told, except he forgot one when he was on the air.

78

Anyway, I brought Mr. Humdinger down in the elevator a few minutes before he was going to go on the air. Collin Wallace, the interviewer, he doesn't like to meet the people he interviews live until the last minute. They had this phony library thing set up in the foyer, and they set up two chairs, for Mr. Humdinger and the Wallace guy, to sit and face each other. Old Mr. Humdinger wasn't at all nervous or anything. He looked real great; I mean he had this great-looking old face with all the lines and wrinkles. This makeup guy wanted to put some junk on his bald head but he wouldn't let him.

I sure didn't like Collin Wallace because he seemed like, I don't know, as if he was doing Humdinger a big favor or something. The first thing he said to Mr. Humdinger was, "You sure look spry and bushy-tailed," or some stuff like that. Old Humdinger didn't say anything to that. He sure didn't have much use for small talk.

I'm sorry. I took the wrong turn, I guess. We're supposed to stay on 202, aren't we? You better navigate because if you don't we'll never get there. Because when I talk I get too excited to watch where I'm supposed to be going.

Oh, yeah. So, as I was saying, there I was, right beside one of the cameras because Mr. Humdinger wanted me around. The director was counting off the seconds and when they went on the air, Collin Wallace gave this phony smile and said, "Happy birthday, Mr. Humdinger. I understand you're celebrating your eighty-ninth; is that right?" And Humdinger comes right back in this great voice—he had this real strong, sort of hoarse voice—and he says, "Never celebrated birthdays. Intend to celebrate deathday, which is another kettle of fish altogether." Wallace sort of smiled but I knew damn well he was pissed off. Anyway he said, "In the twenties you were the philosopher of the people and today the younger generation is discovering you through two of your books reissued in paperback. Could you tell our audience, from the long experience of a full and rich life, something that they can use to enrich their lives? Could you, perhaps, thus summarize your philosophy and the wisdom that you've acquired during your eighty-nine years?"

The camera came real close to Mr. Humdinger then and I couldn't see him so I looked over at the TV set they had and he looked real great. I mean he really did. He sort of had this glow in his eyes, as if he was having the time of his life. And then he let go of them, of the things he was practicing all that day, the clichés. "You can't make a silk purse out of a sow's ear. Look before you leap. People who live in glass houses shouldn't throw stones. A stitch in time saves nine. What goes up must come down. A rolling stone gathers no moss. You can lead a horse to water but you can't make him drink. Count your blessings instead of sheep. Neither a borrower nor a lender be. The bigger they are the harder they fall. The early bird catches the worm. Early to bed and early to rise makes a man healthy, wealthy, and wise. A bird in hand is worth two in the bush. You can't have your cake and eat it

too. If the shoe fits, wear it. Don't take any wooden
nickels. If at first you don't succeed, try, try again.
Nothing ventured nothing gained. Don't cry over spilt
milk. An apple a day keeps the doctor away. Don't
count your chickens before they hatch. It is always
darkest before the dawn. He who laughs last laughs
best."

The camera was on him all that time. And he smiled
and then laughed. Then the camera was on Collin
Wallace and he was clearing his throat and looked
embarrassed as hell. "Well, he said, "those seem to
be . . ." Then there was Mr. Humdinger's face again
in a real close-up as he said, "And don't play dead
before you have to." He was looking straight out and
then his head rolled forward and you could just see
his bald head—and it looked to me like he was taking
a real deep bow. Then Wallace was putting his hand
on Mr. Humdinger's shoulder and I heard what he
said but I thought he was making a stupid joke. He
was saying, "I am afraid those were his last words. Mr.
Humdinger, the great philosopher of the people, is no
more." And then on that monitor screen I saw Mr.
Humdinger slumped in his chair and I looked to the
side and the director was making those circles with
his hand and Wallace was saying, "I did not have the
pleasure of knowing Engebert Humdinger for long,
but in those brief, last moments, and there has been
no more peaceful death, I dare say, witnessed by anyone, I've come to admire him. He had a last message
and he delivered it well. The last thing he said was

perhaps the most meaningful and should become part of our language as the truths contained in the clichés he chose to cite. 'Don't play dead before you have to.' "

And then the screen went black and I heard the director whistle and say, "We've got us a television first."

And that's when I sort of went out of my mind. I hit that guy, right in the mouth, and I think I tried to hit Wallace too. I really don't know what the hell happened to me. I just wanted to beat them up because I didn't want Mr. Humdinger to be dead, I guess.

I don't even remember how I got upstairs but then the next thing I knew I was having this crazy long argument with old Ross. You do? That's what old Ross tried to tell me, that Humdinger died beautifully. He said, "What a great exit he made! To go into that marvelous darkness with a fart into the eye of the color TV camera!" I'm sorry, but that's how he put it. I know it's sort of crude, but he's like that.

What I was mostly arguing with Ross about is what Humdinger meant by piling all those clichés on. I figured that he was mocking the people watching him die but Ross, he said it wasn't so. He said old Humdinger was a foxy old gent and he was telling the people that truth wasn't necessarily profound. He also said that he wouldn't be surprised if Humdinger was making a great point about platitudes, and that he was leaving us with something to think about. That was his main purpose, old Ross felt. You do? You agree with him? Well, the thing is, I wish he had made it plain that dying can be about as noble a thing as a human being can do. But Ross said that's bullshit, living is noble. Dying isn't.

Oh sure. I'd like to talk to you about Charlemagne. Sure I know a lot about what he thinks. He never told you? God, he sure did take it hard! I mean the separation was bad enough, but when you got divorced that's when he sort of began to fall apart. And the thing is, I was too busy to really notice how bad things were getting. I guess all kids feel that way. That's pretty normal. Kids don't want their families broken up. No, they don't want that either. Their parents remarrying is another lousy deal they don't want. I don't know, except kids are changing themselves all the time and when things change around them it might be just too much for them to cope with. Talk about conservatives, little kids are the greatest stick-in-the-mud conservatives in the world.

Charlie is really . . . That's what I call him because he wants me to. Didn't you know he hates his name? That's O.K. I don't think my mom ever knew how much I hated mine. I bet all mothers are like that. I mean, if you notice little things like dirt behind the ears and whether the kid's eaten all his vegetables or not, you can't notice more important things. The way I see it nobody ever says anything intelligent to little kids, so they grow up thinking the way to be is to be dumb. One specific thing? Well, like the truth. How many times does a little kid hear just the simple truth without a lot of bullshit? Sorry. I hope you don't mind me swearing once in a while in front of Charlie. No, as a matter of fact I don't think he's picked up my lousy habit. But maybe when he's older he'll swear too. Swearing doesn't mean anything; that's just the way kids show they're angry or concerned.

I get along O.K. with my parents, I guess. The thing is I like little kids best of all the people. Like a few years ago I had this friend who was four. Actually her brother was my friend but I liked his kid sister because she was about the most beautiful human being I knew. But nobody in her family saw that; nobody listened to her or even looked at her much. She really was great. Oh, for one thing she really had eyes in her head. She'd look at little things like insects and she'd really *see* how perfectly they were made. And could she draw! I don't mean to put Mr. Nordstrom down as an artist, but this little four-year-old kid, she could really paint! But nobody in her family looked at her stuff. It would all get tossed into the garbage or her mother would just say, "What's that?" and not even listen to her answer. One day I came in and she'd done this really great sad painting of a big lady standing next to this little tiny kid who was no bigger than an ant and she was trying, for a half hour, to get her mother to look at it and getting nowhere. And do you know why? Her mother was busy making some damn thing to eat which would end up in the cesspool anyway.

Yeah, that really makes you mad because not every kid is that special or anything. But this one was. And nobody even cared to notice! One day I took a walk with her and it was fall and the leaves were real pretty and she wanted to stop and kiss the prettiest ones. And then, because she felt sorry for the ugly ones, she wanted to kiss those too, for God's sake!

After that walk and because she dug me she wanted to give me something. She didn't have anything handy to give me so do you know what she did? She got on this tricycle of hers and she said to me, "I'll ride my tricycle for you." Man, that really got to me. And then I got to thinking about how groovy it would be if people did things like that for other people. I mean, that could change the whole stupid world, a thing like that!

But she didn't stay that way for long. I mean the next year she went to a crummy kindergarten and they began to work her over. The last time I saw her she was saying to her mother, "I'd like to have a white blouse with a round collar because that's what Suzie and everybody else is wearing." And, you know what, her mother was listening to her! She was actually promising her to get her the dumb blouse! Anyway, she moved away and she's probably a creepy girl by now.

Yeah, that's about the only people I really dig, little kids and old people. With middle-aged people something happens. Like yesterday I walked over to the playground and I was looking at some little kids play on the swings and one little kid, he fell off the swing. And you know what his mother did? She hit him! Where the hell's the logic in that?

That really got me depressed. It's been a damn depressing week—with Mr. Humdinger dying and everything. If we weren't picking up Charlie I don't know what I'd do. You might not know this, Mrs. Nordstrom, but your little kid has been great for me. I mean it's been wonderful having him for a friend. He's about the only human being I can talk to. At Sunnyfield I don't talk so much. I listen. And I try to learn. With Charlie, it's as if I was teaching him something. Anyway, I just wanted to let you know.

xii

O.K., kid, now that the two of us are going to live together for a couple of weeks I better set up some rules. Sure you can make up some rules of your own. Why don't you go first? Because I want to see what you're going to dream up. Oh, O.K., I'll go first.

Just because I'm ten years older . . . What the hell does that matter? O.K., O.K., so just because I'm nine-and-a-half years older than you entitles me to choose if and when I want to be with you or talk with you. When I want to be alone, you leave me alone, O.K.? Because if I don't feel free to be alone I'll start resenting being with you and our whole friendship will go right out of the damn window.

Yeah, that's all the rules. You don't have any? Why not? Come on, Charlie, think up some! You've got one for yourself, not for me? Shoot! Thanks, kid, that's great! I hated it when you made me promise things. You sure are growing up smart. Never ask nobody to promise you anything and you'll never see a promise broken. God, I'm beginning to sound like my old man.

It's funny, me setting up a rule for you, because just yesterday in school I spent a whole day thinking about how rules louse up the world. The first thing that happened was the coach gets on the loudspeaker and he tells us how to breathe. Christ, he's come up with a rule how the hell you're supposed to breathe! Inhale through your nose and exhale through your mouth! You knew it! Damn it, Charlie, don't do it that way! Because! If you breathe in through your nose and there's something stinking around you can smell it!

And listen to this, at lunch, in the cafeteria I went back with my piece of pie and wanted to exchange it for an extra carton of milk. And this cafeteria lady says to me, "There is a rule you can't exchange dessert for milk." I thought she was kidding. But she reaches behind her and brings out this yellowed mimeograph piece of paper and there it is, in black and white, and it says: "Students are not allowed to make exchanges of dessert for milk." And I look at this thing and it's dated 1944, for Christ sake! So I start telling her all the damn things that've happened since then. And I asked her whether it isn't just possible that when that rule was made up the dairies were out on strike or something. And she tells me that all she's doing is following the rule and doing her job. And I ask her if she thinks the rule makes any sense now. And she says, no, because milk probably costs less than a piece of pie. But, she says, it doesn't make any difference, her job is following the rules.

Can you beat that, Charlie! I mean, that's how it is all over the world! Millions of people willing to follow rules they know make no sense! That's how they've loused up my world! Man, when we grow up we just can't do that! We can't go along with that! I'll lose every job I'll ever have because I will refuse to do it.

The way I figure it, it's not only that those damn rules are screwing things up but people actually believe that some rules are laws! Laws! And that's why nobody respects laws—real laws. Man, we're like a bunch of sheep going by some book, memorizing a whole lot of insane rules, made up by God knows who, that don't make any sense.

You know what else happened yesterday? On the way to Sunnyfield I stopped for gas and there was this old guy getting gas at the same station. And he takes a look at my banged-up car and right away he says, "Been driving for over sixty years and never been in no accident." I smiled at him because he was a clean-looking old man and he seemed so damn proud of his record and everything. And then he pulls out of the gas station and I pull out behind him. And what the hell is he doing? He's driving under twenty miles an hour in a fifty-mile zone! And his damn brake lights are on! Pretty soon there's about twenty cars behind us and they start passing us over the white line. So I blow my horn at the old guy, to let him know he's got to go faster, but he doesn't. So I make him pull over and get out and I really give him hell. I yell at him that he's responsible for getting thousands of people killed —splattered across pavement and trees and stuff— people who for sixty years were trying to pass him.

He didn't even get it! He just called me a Commie, a rabble-rouser, and a juvenile delinquent.

Kid, I'm telling you, by the time I got to Sunnyfield I was like foaming at the mouth. And when I told old Ross about that guy he just laughs and says, "Beautiful! What do you want from the old guy? He's a damn hero, a one-man protest movement. He's the only person left in this world who drives a car exactly the same way he drove a horse. Instead of giving him a bad time you should have gotten his autograph."

Man, we argued like mad. When I told him about the cafeteria lady, old Ross says, "Beautiful! She was just upholding an old school tradition."

The thing about old Ross is he turns everything bad into something that could be worse, and all the stuff that I worry about into a sort of a joke. Like, last night, when I was ranting and raving he says to me, "Sit down, honey." And that broke me up because it's from that great scene when W. C. Fields works in this store and this blind guy comes in, and with his cane, feeling his way, he smashes all those light bulbs that are on display. That's one hell of a great scene! Old Ross knows all the Fields flicks backwards. Like once, when I asked him how he figures the world will come to an end, he said, "God will hang out a sign saying 'Closed on account of molasses.'" You'd get it, stupid, if you watched the Fields movie festival like I told you to!

I wish that once in a while old Ross would let me alone when I am telling him things, but he doesn't. He says it's my turn now and I've got a chance to shape up the world. He personally thinks the world's better off now than it ever has been. Like, he says, we made it real tough for anybody to sell us a just cause. From now on it will take a damn genius to make people believe they can kill anybody over anything. And it took us two thousand years to get to this point and he's pretty happy to have stuck around to see it happen. Another thing that he's pretty happy about is the fact that some people are realizing that fear is a contagious disease and it shouldn't be spread around. He says, "Kid, you're coming of age at the right time—at the same time that Man is coming of age. What you're feeling are birth pains, that's all."

Maybe that's right, Charlie. Maybe he wants me to figure out what I want to be, what kind of job I ought to aim for, because he keeps telling me that talk is cheap and what the hell do I intend to do about things. But he agrees with me that I don't have to go to college. Because college is meaningless, that's why! If everybody's got to go to college then college doesn't mean anything. I will too get any job I want because people will be realizing that college doesn't matter; it's what's in your head that does. But, you know what, I wouldn't mind going to a college if there was one where I could major in something like what makes a human being great, or the future. I wouldn't mind majoring in that—in what it's going to be like in thirty years. But they don't have courses like that. So I'm not going to college.

Hey, didn't I tell you? I can't be drafted! No kidding! About a week ago. During the checkup this doctor discovered I've got a heart murmur. I don't know what the hell it is! No, I'm not going to croak. He said I can live to be a hundred. But it's going to keep me out of the Army. How do you like that? I don't know how come I forgot to tell you. I was really excited about that. I'm sorry; it must have slipped my mind.

What's that? Your mother left this for me? Sure I started reading books, about two years ago, for God's sake. Hey, that's really great! I've been meaning to get Humdinger's books out of the library. That's great, your mother buying them for me. She did? Well, I was going to tell you myself. No kidding! But you've never even met him. I don't know, old Ross is about the greatest. You do? A philosopher? You're out of your mind! Nobody hires philosophers, for Christ sake! Most kids your age have a hard time trying to decide whether to be policemen or firemen. You sure are a funny kid, kid. No, I think that's pretty great! Yeah, you go right ahead and be a philosopher; I won't stop you.

What do you mean I could be one too? You're the genius around here. All I'm doing for you, kid, is sabotaging the education you're getting in school, that's all. Because I don't want you to grow up to be a dummy, that's why. The way I figure it, by the time I'm thirty there might be just one single person left in this world who's got a brain in his head. Not me, stupid! You!

Winter and Seventeen

11:35 p.m.

Dear Charlie,

It's New Year's Eve and I feel like writing you, though I'll probably be seeing you in less than a week. I hope skiing is great in Vermont and that you don't mind the chick your father took along. All the people at Sunnyfield loved the cans we painted for them. That sure was swell of your mother to give me $100 for Christmas. I got almost as much from my folks because I told them all I

[2]

need is dough. I'll use all that when I go
around the country this summer with Lennie
Ross. Maybe you can come too, but that's
not promising anything, it's just a thought.
And the reason I've decided to do that is
because of all the things we've been talking
about, Lennie and me.

It's funny how things changed between him
and me. It used to be like a shoot-out every
time I talked to him. He was always gunning
for me, trying to catch me not meaning
what I was saying. He was out to get me each
time I bullshitted. But recently it's been like
he's realized he doesn't have to fight me anymore. Recently he's just been talking to me.

He's got a fireplace in his room and sometimes just the two of us, or sometimes
Hortense and Canali too, we sit in front of it
and rap about everything under the sun.

When you come back I'll tell you about this
trip he took a couple of years ago, across
the country.

The reason he wants me to go with him
on a trip like that is because he thinks that
in the last two years an awful lot has happened to the country, and some of it bad.
He says, "I smell something but I haven't

seen it yet. And what I smell is fear." And
he said the great thing about the country
was the way it was brave and he doesn't
know how the hell it's going to be when it
isn't anymore. He wants to see what fear's
done to people. So we'll check out on things,
as we go. The two of us. Or maybe you too,
the three of us. I've decided to grow my hair
long and I'll probably grow a beard.

The thing is I've been cutting my hair short
because I'm probably the only straight kid
left in the world and I didn't want the hip
kids to think I'm not. But I met this guy
who just hitchhiked over from Oregon and
he told me that I wouldn't find out a damn
thing unless my hair was long when I went
across the country. And that's because people
have gotten to the point where they don't
give a damn what you are or what you think
as long as you look neat and clean. And he
thinks it's a real sick scene but that it's got
its own merit. "If you want to feel what it's
like to be a nigger in America," he said, "all
you've got to do is grow your hair down to
your shoulders."

Anyway I'll see for myself if he's right.
Ross thinks it's a great idea, my getting all

[4]

hairy, because it will be like fooling all those dummies, to look like a hippie and not be one. Ross is a bum and he sort of looks like one but I bet there has never been anyone like him before. It all shows you that you can't tell a book by its cover, which is another one old Humdinger forgot to tell them about.

See you soon, and don't break a leg on those skis.

Byron

That's what I'm going to tell you about! Throw another log on that fire, will ya? No, I'll do it. I don't want you breaking your other leg. Still itches like hell, huh? What did you want to ski down that slope for? No, I never did. I don't know how the hell I survived my whole damn childhood without breaking anything, but I did.

Idaho, that's where I want to go with Ross most of all. He's got his friend living there, on this big spread with horses and everything. This guy's name is Roy Miller and he's got a daughter, my age, that Ross thinks I'll really go for. No, that's not the reason! I want to meet her old man for one thing. Ross says he pioneered that part of Idaho. Like there was nothing but sagebrush growing there when he came as a young guy. Now he's got ten kids and Ross says they're the greatest. I told you, Charlie! We just might take you along. But I'm not promising a thing. And that's a promise. So, do you want to hear about it or not?

Well, when Ross was staying there, a couple of years ago, this group of hippie-like people came. There were about a dozen of them and they had a few kids with them and this blind guy, who was like their leader. Anyway, they asked Mr. Miller's permission to settle on a piece of his property—in this sunny field. The blind guy said that he had a vision about this place, and they would like to live and build log cabins there. Mr. Miller asked him what kind of a vision and it's really weird what this blind guy told him.

These people, they used to be real hippies in San Francisco, and they used to get wrecked all the time but one day this guy, who wasn't blind yet, had a real bad trip. He was listening to this song by The Mourning Reign. Hey, remind me to bring over the record of this rock musical they did; it's called *Through the Looking Glass*. Anyway, he was listening over and over again to this song that goes:

It's a great huge
game of chess
that's being played
all over the world . . .

And suddenly he began to have this vision. He actually *felt* that he was in the future. And it was like twenty-five years from now and all the kids in the world were just going to rock festivals and getting stoned and that's all they were doing. Nobody under thirty was doing any work or anything. And pot was legal. Getting stoned was legal and nobody was hassling them, and they were left alone doing their thing.

And by then there was no President in the United States and no Congress or Supreme Court. The whole country was run by the Officers, from the police and the Army. And most of the other countries in the world were run that way too. Well, there were a lot of people in the world. So all the Officers got together and decided that they better do something about the overpopulation problem because there were over seven billion people by then and they decided that they were going to blow up part of Africa and part of Asia to

97

make more room for people. But they never got around to doing that. They didn't have to. They solved the overpopulation problem another way.

When the Officers came back they found that things had changed. The young weren't the same anymore. They'd stopped grooving on music and on drugs and now they had little kids with them.

There was one hell of a lot of little kids. And they seemed to be leading those bigger kids around. The little kids seemed like guardians or something, and the older ones kept repeating this line from the Bible, "And a little child shall lead them." They were saying that the world's got to be changed and the little kids were going to do the changing. But all those little kids, they weren't saying anything or doing anything but just walking around. And everything was coming to a standstill; the traffic was piling up and nobody could work because the kids were all over the place—inside churches and office buildings and everywhere except inside schools or their homes.

It was like an invasion, except there were no guns and all the kids were just walking—the little ones leading the older ones. And this guy with the vision, he said it was the most beautiful thing he ever saw—just this whole mess of kids walking around.

What the Officers decided to do then was to kill off all the kids. Actually they planned to kill off every single human being on earth under thirty. So they killed them all and it took four months. The massacre took four months. And this guy, in his vision, he saw it all. And it was like he lived through those four months of killing and he witnessed all of them dying, even the babies that were being born. And it was so horrible . . . No, he went blind later!

Anyway, after that there was no more overpopulation problem. But the Officers discovered they had another problem. All the people who saw or heard of the killing of the young, they were in a state of shock. They wouldn't work; they couldn't think or do anything. And nobody was afraid of punishments or threats or anything. Nobody cared about anything at all. And it was like that all over the world, as if nobody could stop mourning.

And that was when the Scientists came into the picture. The Scientists invented a drug that made the people forget the massacre of the young. And this drug, they called it *Killium*, and they distributed it through the water supplies. And from then on the Scientists ruled together with the Officers.

After a couple of years people began to have children again, but just one per couple was all that was allowed. The ones who were born then were different from the children born before. Babies didn't cry and a lot of them died for no reason that anybody could understand. And those who lived, they were sort of private and their eyes were almost transparent as if they could see through their parents. And they didn't talk much and they never laughed and they didn't play any games. And they didn't seem to need anything like love. And when they were five they were given some sort of pills to pep them up but it only made them sadder.

By then it was the beginning of the twenty-first century and everybody in the United States lived in huge cities under plastic domes, so that they could breathe because pollution was real bad—but it was all sucked out from those domes. It was easy for the Officers to watch everybody under those domes. Some of those cities were all white and some were all black and some were mixed.

And out in the country computers were cultivating the earth and mechanized trucks were bringing in the food and hardly anybody was allowed to go outside those city complexes except for the Officers and the Scientists.

Kids didn't go to school because they were learning from television and computers. But then some of them began to disappear. A few were found and they were brought back but they wouldn't say where it was that they'd been going to. Some were found dead on the roads, run over by those mechanized trucks. But many of them were never found, though they looked for them all over.

Their parents didn't know what made them want to leave and they wondered about where they would possibly want to go. Nobody living in those cities could imagine living anywhere else because it was comfortable and safe and everybody had everything they needed. But by then nobody was writing or painting or making music because the Officers and the

Scientists had decided all those things were dangerous because they made some people special, and these Officers and Scientists wanted everybody to be equal because the United States was still a democracy.

Nobody suspected that those kids could be influenced from the outside. But the kids could sort of sense the thoughts of other people. They had this gift, ESP, which means extrasensory perception. If you've got it, you can transmit and receive thoughts from other people. Now, this is where the vision really became weird. Because this guy, for the first time, found himself a participant in his own vision. I mean, before then he was like an observer—or a witness who didn't take part in any of this—but suddenly he was in his own vision.

Anyway, the kids were receiving thoughts from this group of people, who lived near a sunny field somewhere in Idaho, in a place that was going to be used once, but never was a nuclear test site. So those runaway kids—and some of them came from the black cities and some from the all white and some from the mixed ones—they were guided to this place in Idaho by the people who lived there. And the guy who was having the vision, he was one of them!

They had to cross a country that they'd never even heard about, and it was nothing like it is today. Near the cities everything was destroyed by pollution. The waters were poisoned and the fish and vegetation and wildlife—it was all dead. And you know what, Charlie, in his vision the guy could actually smell the decay! Anyway, further on were those endless fields. All cul-

101

tivated by computers. And still further was this wild country and it really frightened the kids, but those people in Idaho, they kept telling them in their minds not to be afraid.

Those kids met other kids. They all walked together, but they didn't speak to each other. And when the first of them reached this sunny field in the valley— that's where the guy's vision ended. Yeah, that was it! He just saw those kids stepping into this sunny field and that was the last—the very last thing he ever saw! Because he came out of that vision blind.

Yeah! That's exactly what he did! He described this place to his friends. They believed the whole vision, that it was really going to happen, and they went looking for this place he saw. And they found it on Mr. Miller's land. Oh, sure! He let them stay!

When Ross was there, on Mr. Miller's land, they were beginning to build their log cabins. He said they're really great people, very gentle and sweet and their kids are the greatest because they're brought up to believe they have a special mission in life. It's like a religion with them, except they are not out to convert anybody to believe what they believe.

I don't know. Maybe something like that could happen. No, Ross doesn't think it's possible. He has this great faith in people. He really doesn't think anything like that could ever happen in this country. I don't know, kid. That's mainly why I want to go across the country with Ross. To find out if it could. No, Mr. Miller doesn't believe it could happen either.

But he isn't afraid of those people's beliefs. He lets his kids play with their kids and Ross says it's the greatest —seeing those kids playing together on that sunny field.

Yeah, that's what's so weird. It gives me the shivers. I mean, there it is, that old people's home called Sunnyfield and out there, somewhere in Idaho, there is that other sunny field. No, they're off drugs now. They're just grooving on life, or that's what Ross says they're doing.

Ross spent a lot of time talking to those people. What he likes best about them is the way they're bringing up their kids. They never lie to them, and they believe that a kid, instinctively, is going to grow up fine. And since it's like a commune, everybody shares everything with everybody; they don't get jealous of each other. And Ross says nobody ever gets angry or afraid. This blind guy, he has like a theory that if you start feeling guilty about things you become poisoned, and he doesn't feel guilty about dropping out of society. He says they're doing their thing to preserve it.

Don't bug me about that. Look, even if you don't go with us, I'll tell you all about it. Sure I want to meet Denise. The way Ross was raving about that whole family I'd be a fool not to want to meet them. And man, do I want to talk to that blind guy! I want him to tell me more about that vision. Hey, I hope you won't get any nightmares about that, Charlie! That's good. Dreams are great but nightmares are pretty awful. I'm glad you don't get any anymore.

Spring and Seventeen

What the hell did you do it for? If you expect me to forgive you for that, Lennie, you're damn wrong. You lousy traitor! Only last week I was going to tell you that you ought to stop fooling around and ask Hortense Meister to marry you before you croak. She was in love with you and you knew it. Did you ever let her in on that, that you knew? You told me she was your kind of woman and you started laughing then. And, damn it, I knew what you were chuckling about; you didn't want to seem foolish. Because you dug her, didn't you? I'd have been your best man, don't you know that?

Why did you give Canali that argument when he said that Sunnyfield was the last stop on a trip with nowhere else to go? So where the hell did you go? And that stuff you gave me about my not knowing what happens in the dark hours of the night. You were planning the whole deal, weren't you? You were croaking on me! How the hell do you think I'm going to make it now? You were the only person who could have done something for me. Those arguments I gave you, they didn't mean a thing. Each time, on the way home, or the next day in school, I'd think over what we argued about and I was buying. Yeah! I was buying the stuff you were selling me. You won each one of those arguments we had but I couldn't tell you that because I thought you'd be too stuck-up if you knew. And I'm sorry now I never did tell you. And I never minded you putting me down. I loved it when you said to me, "I never learned anything from a kid I couldn't unlearn." But I am not going to unlearn what I've learned from you. And the most important thing I learned from you is that I've got to be the best Byron Carmichael I can be. And I'll do it, just like you said. I'll go looking for God in people. Because you were right about that too. People aren't perfect; it's not their job to be. But if I don't find traces of God in people, I won't find God anywhere. But what did you do such a cruddy thing for? You could have waited longer before giving it up. Hell, you were the one who told me life was beautiful. Why couldn't you have hung on? You know what I'll remember best out of all the things you said to me? You said that life boils down to how much do we pay, with what, for what.

But you also said that all there was to us was getting born, loving, and dying—and we only have control over one of those. So maybe you didn't mean to die on me. God, I knew you'd die on me one day but, Lennie, we were going to bum around the country together!

I was not through learning from you, don't you know that!

i

You know kid, I used to think the same thing. I used to think that this street was the sickest street in the world. But I don't anymore. I think Forty-second Street is about the saddest street in the world. I used to think that all those porno stores and all those dirty movie theaters were the lousiest places. But I've been trying to figure this whole deal out. I mean there must be enough perverts around to support those places, for God's sake! What the hell are we becoming, a goddamn nation of perverts? It's not only this miserable street, the perverts are moving about; they're invading my whole damn world. I mean it, kid; I really feel sick about it. I mean, how the hell are you ever going to make it with girls? I mean, by the time you're old enough to have sex all those stinking pornographers and all those stinking perverts would have made it so foul that you won't even know what a really great thing it used to be once.

No, don't look at that lady, kid. She's just a poor

crazy old lady and there are enough stupid shits looking and laughing at her. I don't know why nobody
takes care of her. I don't know what the hell is happening. I mean, she should be taken care of. She should
have somebody to look after her. Like what's the use
of being so damn rich and having all those billion-
dollar buildings and stuff if we have ladies like that
walking all alone with their paper bags?

I don't know where the hell I want to go. Where the
hell do you want to go? A zoo? Maybe that's part of
the answer. What the hell do people want with zoos?
Shit, we lock up some beautiful wild animals in cages
and the next thing we know we're all screwed up. I
haven't figured it out yet! Give me time! It's just an
idea, but maybe it's part of something.

Look what you made me do. I was going to show
you the big city and we were going to have fun and
here I am getting mad at the whole damn world again.
Man, old Ross certainly was right about it when he
said that I haven't got a chance in hell of making it as
a human being if I ever stop laughing. But who the
hell is laughing? I mean, everybody seems to have
stopped laughing. Look at this crowd! They look
ridiculous but nobody's laughing at themselves.

Man, I must be the only person in the world who
has to chase after a bum to give him money. No, he
didn't say anything to me. He only looked sort of
scared. I must have startled him. He wasn't old enough
to qualify for Sunnyfield. What do you mean? I always
gave handouts to bums, way before I ever met old
Ross. To tell you the absolute truth, it only happened

once before. But I intend to always do it. I mean where the hell have all the beggars gone? Like in the Middle Ages you could really practice charity, but all we've got left are our bums. Besides, I admire bums and would just as soon give them some money for booze than some church or some organized charity. Because! It takes a certain kind of gut to turn your ass on jobs and security and comfort when you're not a kid.

Did you see that? That's pretty funny. That joke on the wall. "Why are Polish dogs flat-headed? From chasing after parked cars." But old Ross said there's nothing really that great being written on walls anymore since some idiot professor decided to teach graffiti for college credits. You can't find wisdom on the walls anymore, just jokes and obscenities. That's about all you get off walls nowadays.

What do you mean it looks dirty inside? If a joint where I want to get a hot dog was to smell like a damn hospital the hot dog would stink. Two, with everything on them. Hey, look at that guy, over at the counter there. He must be some hot-shot executive. But what did he order? A pepperoni pizza. Like a kid. Hortense Meister was sure right about that—about it being tougher to be grown-up than to be a kid. She said that adults are just a bunch of kids who aren't allowed life belts. And if nobody taught them to swim they have one hell of a hard time keeping afloat. So Odman, Rice, Goodlet, and Appleton are petty and never say anything! It might be that they've been drowned by life because nobody bothered to teach them how to keep afloat.

I don't know where the hell we're going! I just want to walk around for a while. Let's just walk, to the Bowery maybe. Jesus, but New York is still a beautiful city! How come they let it go to the dogs like that? Look at all that garbage. I mean, we're ass-deep in newspapers and crap.

I've got this real creepy feeling about this place. In a couple more years all the regular people are going to hightail it out of here. And who are they going to leave the city to? To a bunch of punk muggers, junkies and porno merchants and perverts and crazy people, that's who! Man, if I ever lived in New York City, I'd fight for it. I wouldn't let a bunch of creeps inherit the place.

You know what the trouble with these people is? You're right, kid! They're afraid! Of what? I don't know either. But they're afraid of getting involved. Of that too. Sure, they get mugged in broad daylight but that's because other people just stand back. Don't those creeps realize that they've got to be involved or else they'll be down flat on their own backs some day with somebody's knife up their ribs?

Hey, don't let me rave again because I came to New York to enjoy myself and to make you see it the way Ross saw it. You know what he said about New York City? He said it's a great combination of a sellout freak show and unattended Resurrection. He meant nobody notices miracles in this city; all they see are the stupidities. We were going to start off on our trip right here. Oh, hell, Charlie! I miss that guy! I miss him so bad!

Summer and Seventeen

Yeah, dad, I gave Mr. Nelson that letter you wrote apologizing for my hair. He said I should say hallo to you and that I shouldn't worry about the hair, not until I get hired anyway. Yeah, dad, I took it. I don't think I passed. I mean, did you really think I'd pass that Executive Ability Test? Oh, mom! Well, for one thing they asked me, "Do you have trouble making decisions?" And I said, "Yes and no." Another question was about how would I feel if I had to fire somebody and I said I'd feel terrible and couldn't probably do it. No, dad, it's not that I wouldn't want to work for the New Jersey Transit. I wouldn't mind being a bus driver like you. But, don't you see, I've got other things I've got to do first before I can get a job.

110

Oh, mom, we've been over that so many times! Why would you feel ashamed at the Rosary meeting? I sure would know what to tell the ladies about that! So what? Is that so terrible to be the only mother with a child who isn't going to be a college grad? Well, tell me! What's so terrible about that? But I don't feel proud of being different! I care what I think of myself, not what other people think of me. I just don't feel that I'd get anything out of college! You don't have to pay a few thousand dollars a year to meet people! Dad, it's not that. I don't want to be a winner or a loser. I want to be somewhere in between. Well, maybe that's something that's wrong with the country, not me, not having a place for anybody in between.

Sure, I know what I want to do this summer! I want to go across the country! O.K., I wouldn't hitchhike. I'd take my car. It runs fine; it would get me there and back. Look, did I have an accident yet? A single accident? No! I can't help it if people run into me for Chri . . . She did, mom? Where did she hear me swearing? I bet her Johnny never swore in his life. I don't know, mom; all I know is that he's called the Rapist of the Ramapo Valley, that's all. Oh, sure, I was only kidding.

Now, the way I figure it, if I go across the country I'd know what I'd want to do with my life. How? It would help me decide. I'd see what's going on and what if anything ought to be done about it. I mean, it just might be that this whole country's going down the drain. I sure would! I'd try to do something about it!

I'd go to Washington. No, dad! I wouldn't be your President. I'd get a job there. Maybe with our Congressman or Senator. No, mom, I wouldn't need a college education because I'd just as soon be a messenger boy. That way I could snoop around and see how things could have gotten fouled up and how, legally, we can get them unfouled up.

God, mom! I could never get through law school! And Lincoln would have been just as great a President as he was without studying law. He was a terrible lawyer anyway. Well, wasn't he? I don't know. I thought he was. Gee, I don't care how much money I'd make! I really don't give much of a damn about money because there is nothing I want to buy anyway. That's my right! Not caring! If you're ashamed of me, that's your problem, not mine!

I'm not screaming at her, dad. I'm trying to talk to you for a change. I mean, tomorrow, I'll be eighteen years old! And how many times in all those years did we ever have a serious talk together? Why don't you just listen to me for a change? That's what I'd like for my birthday! Five minutes of uninterrupted attention right now. Can you afford it?

Sure, that's what I really want! But that's the whole point; I want the five minutes to convince you that I'm right in wanting to spend the summer going across the country. So how about being open-minded and letting me? Look, a lot of kids are leaving home without their parents' permission. I want to be different about it. I want your permission. And if I owe you respect, I'm trying to earn it from you, right this minute.

O.K., so just take my hair. That's funny, dad! Help yourself. You're getting bald as an eagle; pretty soon you'll be protected by law. The American bald eagle is protected by law. You'd qualify. Hey, that's a good one, dad! I must remember that one: "You sure your beard isn't covering a terminal case of acne?" Where did you steal that one from?

Come on! Give me a chance. Just five minutes! All right, so my stupid hair is like a symbol. I mean, does it really matter how long or short it is? Am I any different or bad because of it? Well, that's just it! I'm not a hippie and I don't take drugs! But people think I do.

What's so difficult to understand? By wearing my hair long I'm making people realize they're judging me without knowing me. It's about the most important thing to make them realize! How the hell do you think it all started with the Jews in Germany or the Negroes here? Everybody was just looking at people and didn't bother knowing anything about them; they just dumped them all together. God, what has got to matter is what you think and not how you look! I mean, it's what's under the hair that matters!

That's part of what I want to find out—if people care what you think or only how you look. Because if they only care about how you look we're in real trouble, because any clean-cut cat can come along and they will listen to him just because he's clean-cut. And he could be like a madman, like a Hitler or a Stalin, don't you see that?

There is a whole lot more I want to find out. I mean,

the way it looks around here, people don't even think that there are alternatives. Yeah, sometimes I use a big word; is that O.K. with you, dad? So there are other alternatives; you don't have to choose between kids who take acid and those who take antacid. Between the SDS jerks and the Wallace idiots. Between black bigots and white bigots. I mean, hell, people seem to think that you either have to burn a flag or wave it.

I happen to think that we're better than any other people in the world, and other people are still looking to us for answers. And maybe we're not asking ourselves questions. Because there is something wrong in this country; something got derailed and I want to find out what. And what are we afraid of? I want to find out why is that, because we are. I don't want to get married and bring up kids among a whole bunch of weirdos. Don't you see it? I've got to learn about this country I live in.

And this summer might be my only chance to do that. Before I know the general direction I'm going to aim for, before I get a job, I've got to do it! All I know is that next year it will be too late for me to find out for myself. Or maybe next year I won't want to find out. And that would be a damn shame because I don't want to play dead before I have to.

I wouldn't be going alone. Well, I'd like to take Charlie with me. I think she would let him go. We've got it all planned, how to con her into letting him go. If she objects to just the two of us going alone Mrs.

Meister said she'd come with us. Oh, for God's sake! Who would be better qualified than a teacher? She's not. She's old but there's nothing wrong with her, physically or mentally!

I have enough money. Mrs. Nordstrom gave me some for a graduation present and I've saved some. Just for this trip. So, what do you say?

I knew you'd understand! I even bet Charlie you would. And he bet me his mother would let him come along. Hey, thanks! The thing is I'd really be finding things out for you too. And if I find out that everything's gotten really rotten wrong—so bad that it can't even be fixed—I'd let you in on it. If we're in some real evil place, then we could move on. To Idaho. There's a place where we could go and live. No, I won't tell you about it until we have to go there. But I hope we never have to. Sure I'd take you. Because you're my parents and I give a damn about you, that's why.

Oh, mom! I was always a good boy. Didn't you know that? God! Swearing is like long hair. It doesn't mean a damn thing. It's what you're saying, while you're swearing, that matters. Sure. I promise. I'll try to stop swearing so damn much. I'll practice on the trip.

Hey, I've got to go call Charlie. He's been sitting on his ass all evening waiting for me to call.

92978

DATE DUE

HR 01 75	FEB 21 '79		
AR 24 75	APR 23 81		
AP 9 75	DEC 15 81		
MY1 75	JUL 30 1982		
MY15 75	JUL 15 1993		
MY15 75			
JY7 - 75			
OC16 75			
MR 21 76			
FACULTY			
JUL 28 77			
MAR 3 '78			